"What Exactly Can I Do?"

Kelly asked.

"Be on guard for the newshounds. Some of them have incredible gall."

The rancor of Blair's comment about members of her own profession killed any slight possibility of confidence and brought back all the misery of her deception.

"How about a nightcap before I walk you back?"

"No!" she objected swiftly.

"You're a fraud." The low words were spoken with a cold distinctness that slashed through the shaky foundation of Kelly's composure. She teetered on the steep, lonely precipice of fear, trying desperately not to crash to her destruction.

CAROLE HALSTON
is the wife of a sea captain and ~~~~~~ ~~~ stories while her husband is ~~~~~~~~~~~~~~ ~~aracters frequently ~~~~~~~~~~~~~~~~~~~~~~ ure and enjoymen~~~~~~

Dear Reader:

During the last year, many of you have written to Silhouette telling us what you like best about Silhouette Romances and, more recently, about Silhouette Special Editions. You've also told us what else you'd like to read from Silhouette. With your comments and suggestions in mind, we've developed SILHOUETTE DESIRE.

SILHOUETTE DESIREs will be on sale this June, and each month we'll bring you four new DESIREs written by some of your favorite authors—Stephanie James, Diana Palmer, Rita Clay, Suzanne Simms and many more.

SILHOUETTE DESIREs may not be for everyone, but they are for those readers who want a more sensual, provocative romance. The heroines are slightly older—women who are actively involved in their careers and the world around them. If you want to experience all the excitement, passion and joy of falling in love, then SILHOUETTE DESIRE is for you.

I'd appreciate any thoughts you'd like to share with us on new SILHOUETTE DESIRE, and I invite you to write to us at the address below:

Karen Solem
Editor-in-Chief
Silhouette Books
P.O. Box 769
New York, N.Y. 10019

CAROLE HALSTON
Undercover Girl

Silhouette *Romance*
Published by Silhouette Books New York
America's Publisher of Contemporary Romance

Other Silhouette Books by Carole Halston

Stand-in Bride
Love Legacy
Keys to Daniel's House

SILHOUETTE BOOKS, a Simon & Schuster Division of
GULF & WESTERN CORPORATION
1230 Avenue of the Americas, New York, N.Y. 10020

ISBN: 0-671-57152-4

First Silhouette Books printing May, 1982

10 9 8 7 6 5 4 3 2 1

Map by Tony Ferrara

America's Publisher of Contemporary Romance

Printed in the U.S.A.

Undercover
Girl

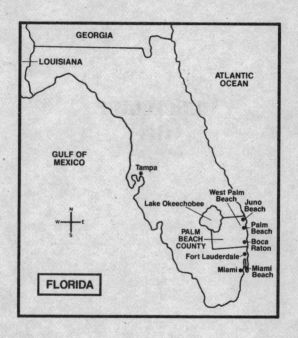

Chapter One

"Ah, here you are, Kelly. My dear, you're much too young and lovely to hide away in a corner. There's time enough for that when you're old and gray like me."

"But that's ridiculous, Mr. Curtis," Kelly murmured, her cheeks flushing with embarrassment at the amused looks leveled in their direction. "You're not that old!" Her color deepened at the sardonic gleam in his eyes, and she hated herself for acting like such a small-town idiot in front of her boss.

Much of her discomfiture stemmed not from shyness or lack of self-confidence, but from the sarcastic comments she had overheard a few minutes ago from some of the other staff members who, like herself, worked to produce the nightly television news program *The People Element*.

"Wish I had big brown eyes and blond hair—bet I could get me a promotion *fast!*"

"You don't say! The big man can't take his eyes off

our new young research assistant. I'll bet he's planning to do a little research himself before the night's over!"

Kelly had cringed at the brittle laughter, and smarting at the unfairness of the snide remarks, she had gone to hide in the corner where Stan Curtis soon found her. By now she should be used to the accusations that she exploited her exceptional looks in order to garner the high attainments—including excellent grades and scholastic honors all through high school and college—which in reality she had worked very hard to achieve. There was no denying that men found her extremely attractive. The striking combination of velvety brown eyes screened by dark lashes and silken platinum blond hair attracted male attention wherever she went, and her tall curvaceous figure added to her feminine allure.

Tonight she had been thrilled at the opportunity to meet Stan Curtis on a relaxed, informal basis. The older man still had a vitality that was almost overwhelming in close quarters. For the past six months she had only glimpsed him through the open door of his office or in the studio. He was usually surrounded by other people and much too busy and important a man to stop and chat with an underling like herself, fresh out of college with her communications degree.

The party tonight was in his French Quarter apartment and included the whole staff of the popular local program he produced, plus some of the other luminaries of Channel 10 in New Orleans. Kelly had been terribly excited about rubbing elbows with people who had already attained success in that magical world of television entertainment. But she had arrived at the party with every intention of fading contentedly into the background, listening and watching.

What a false expectation that had proved to be! As fate would have it, Stan Curtis himself opened the door and stopped still in the middle of a smooth, perfunctory greeting. His gaze swept over her from head to toe in a scrutiny that brought added color to cheeks already reddened by the damp March wind gusting off the Mississippi River just a few blocks away. Was there something wrong with her attire? Some tentative questions about what to wear to the party had elicited the information that at gatherings of this sort one would find everything from designer jeans to tuxedos. Her own choice after literally days of deliberation was a black velvet skirt and matching blazer over a white silk blouse.

The outfit was the most expensive in her wardrobe, but one she had justified on the basis of its versatility and timelessness, not to mention the elegance it imparted to her tall slender form. When she had turned to the triple mirrors in the fitting room, it was hard to believe the exquisite creature she saw there was really herself. She would have stolen that suit, if necessary, when in reality she had to give up lunches and all small self-indulgences for months in order to pay for it.

Before tonight it had been too special to wear, hanging in her closet carefully protected by plastic wrappings, a modern Cinderella's gown. Now, standing in the open doorway of Stan Curtis' apartment, she felt the way Cinderella must have felt on the threshold of a glittering world. And this talented man, whom she had admired from a distance for the past six months, was gazing with apparent fascination at the girl whose windblown hair was as pale as spun gold around her shoulders. Her eyes were huge velvet pools of darkness spangled with the slight apprehension which arose out of her uncertainty. Her lips were parted and her breath came unevenly, not just from nervous anticipation but from her dash through narrow dark streets where danger seemed to lurk at every turn.

"Shut that door!" someone called from the room beyond the small foyer, and the silent spell was broken. Stan Curtis drew Kelly inside with solicitous words of apology for keeping her standing in the cold dampness.

He had escorted her personally into the crowded

living room and shaken off the attempts to detain him as he threaded his way to the next room, where a bar was set up in one corner. It hadn't been easy to talk with all the noise. The combination of human voices, laughter and modern jazz throbbing from the concealed stereo speakers created a deafening din. But somehow Stan Curtis extracted from Kelly her name and position with the station. She expected him to lose all interest as soon as he learned just how unimportant she was among the assembly, but he kept her firmly beside him, introducing her to countless people, some of whom she knew by sight and reputation.

It was during one of the brief times she found herself separated from him that she heard the cutting remarks which sent her off to a far corner of the apartment, afraid the humiliation would show in her eyes. Underneath the anger and resentment at the unfairness of the catty remarks was the uncomfortable awareness of a certain truth in the suspicions cast upon Stan Curtis' motives in showing her so much attention. Although he must be over sixty, many young women would still willingly fall into his bed in the hope he could help them to advance in the world of television. The thought spoiled her pleasure in the evening.

The opportunity to brood was short-lived, though, for he soon found her and pulled her back into the mainstream of the party. Sometime long after midnight, the crowd rapidly dwindled and she realized with a shock that she was one of the last people there. She was about to make her own departure when Allen Loftlen, the head meteorologist at Channel 10, suggested the hangers-on all go to the Café du Monde for coffee and *beignets*.

The few remaining guests unanimously agreed and Kelly found herself swept along with them as they trooped out of the apartment and down to the street to their separate cars. The blustery wind combined with a pelting rain discouraged even the most hardy souls from walking.

The Café du Monde wasn't far, and Kelly soon found herself sipping the rich *café au lait,* a strong French Market coffee laced with hot milk, and munching *beignets,* piping hot pastries sprinkled with powdered sugar. Gripped by a sensation of unreality that this whole night could be happening to her, Kelly Lindsay from Houma, Louisiana, she listened to the talk at her table, marveling to herself. It's really true, she thought, important topics are discussed, momentous decisions are made around tables like this one in the most casual circumstances.

Stan Curtis was seated on her left, discussing upcoming features for the television show he produced. The other four people crowded around the small table were all influential members of the staff, people whose opinions carried weight. Joan Talbot, the female reporter on *The People Element* whose specialty was interviewing people involved in one unusual pursuit or another, lamented, "I'd give my right arm to do the Palm Beach thing, but it's just too risky. Stan, you know the odds against getting inside those high walls separating the super rich from the rest of the world. It's a great idea to get an inside view into the world of the elite, but it just won't work." She shrugged regretfully and took a sip of her coffee.

"Joan's probably right, Stan," Randy Prescott agreed in the resonant voice so well-known to television viewers in New Orleans. "The press is anathema to people like that. It's practically an undercover job, as melodramatic as that sounds, and will take a lot of time. Weeks, maybe even months, to get the real picture. Who can afford the gamble? It might be the chance of the century, and then again it might be a magnificent bust!" He snubbed out his cigarette and waited for a reply.

Kelly sat mesmerized, looking with wide brown eyes from one face to another, totally oblivious to the sprinkling of powdered sugar on her black velvet suit. A crazy idea was forming inside her head, an idea so insane she dared not even say it aloud. Then Stan spoke.

"I'm afraid you two are right. But I hate to give up the idea! It's an assignment for someone with nothing to lose, and that means, unfortunately, someone without experience. Someone has to be willing to drop everything to go down there and figure out some way to get the job done. Who do we have who could and would do it?"

"*I would!*"

All the eyes swung to Kelly's flushed face, and she suddenly had the overpowering urge to slide down under the table. They didn't have to say what they were thinking because the unanimous question shone in their eyes: Who is this anyway?

With quick perception Stan took control of the situation. "Some of you probably haven't had a chance to get to know Kelly. She's been on our research staff for six months now. She has a communications degree from LSU."

The faces were unimpressed with this revelation, but they were too polite to offend the big man, who seemed quite taken with the young girl. But their unspoken opinion was that she probably didn't have a brain in her pretty head.

Kelly smarted under the obvious skepticism in their expressions. The offer to take on the job had been an impulse and she wished fervently now she had kept her big mouth shut, but it was too late to take the words back. A measure of pride prompted her to speak with a coolness she didn't feel.

"As Stan said, it's a job for someone with nothing to lose and no experience. I probably fit that bill better than anybody else connected with the show. Of course,

I realize I'd be on my own. In the event that everything backfired and I got myself in a bind, the station wouldn't take any responsibility for me."

After a thoughtful pause, one question after another was fired at her until she realized with a shock they were actually considering her offer! An hour later she stood in the living room of her own apartment, dazed with the incredible new development in her life. She had volunteered to go to Palm Beach, one of the most exclusive settlements of the wealthy in the entire world, and get a feature on the inside view of their lives. It was unbelievable! Crazy!

Gradually a current of excitement possessed her, overwhelming her insecurities and doubts. This was her big opportunity to make a name for herself. If she pulled off this assignment, she would be well on her way to a career in television journalism. It would be worth the risk. And somehow she would be successful too. She just knew she would! She had never failed to accomplish any goal she had ever set for herself, and she wouldn't fail now.

Chapter Two

Kelly opted to take Highway 90 along the southern coast of Mississippi rather than Interstate 10. She loved the drive from Bay St. Louis to Pascagoula, sand beaches and blue-gray waters of the Gulf of Mexico on her right and to the left stately old white houses with huge screened verandas and oak trees bowing under the weight of Spanish moss.

She sighed, remembering the hectic preparations of the last few days. She had had to advertise for someone to sublet her apartment and it wasn't until the last minute that an offbeat-looking woman turned up claiming to be an artist in town for a few months. Kelly wasn't at all happy leaving the apartment in her care, but Jeanne Simpson across the hall had promised to keep an eye on things and notify the landlord if anything suspicious happened.

Then there had been the briefing sessions with Stan and some of the other top-brass staff members. Finally, after packing her bags, withdrawing the bulk of her modest savings and buying traveler's checks, she was on her way.

Stan had offered to pay her a portion of her salary while she was off on this job, but she had refused for reasons not at first clear to herself. Now she realized she didn't want the pressure of being on a paid assignment until she had proved her worth. As it was, she was leaving New Orleans with the understanding that she could take as long as she needed to get the story and her job would be waiting for her when she returned. Meanwhile, she was entirely on her own. If she met with success and the feature was acceptable, she would be well compensated for her time and work. If not, she would return to her job having cost no one except herself any expense.

At Mobile, her common sense took over and she followed the signs directing her to Interstate 10, rejecting the impulse to continue along the coast on the scenic two-lane Highway 98. Resigning herself to the monotony of north Florida, she reflected that, barring mishaps, she would be able to drive half the distance that day and arrive in Palm Beach the following day.

Her one contact there was Philip Lawson, the editor of a Sunday supplement magazine for a West Palm Beach newspaper and a former colleague of Stan's some time during his earlier newspaper days. Stan had suggested she get in touch with Lawson immediately upon arrival so that he could direct her to a motel that was respectable without having outlandish rates.

That night she stopped at a Holiday Inn located right off the Interstate, too exhausted to drive any farther. After a sandwich in the coffee shop, she went to her room and telephoned Philip Lawson. His voice was deep and pleasantly masculine, and she guessed he must be in his early forties. After telling him her present whereabouts and estimating the time of her arrival the following afternoon, she wrote down his instructions for their first meeting place. He would help her locate a motel and take her to dinner.

Twenty-four hours later she faced him across the table of a small quiet restaurant in West Palm Beach and noted he was younger than she had expected, probably late thirties. On the whole, he was not exceptional-looking, with an average height and build, brown hair and eyes. His droll manner of speaking and air of bored self-confidence made him something other than just ordinary.

He looked as if nothing in the world would have the capacity to surprise him, as if he had seen and done everything conceivable without having been impressed. Kelly relaxed during the meal, entertained by his amusing insights into Palm Beach County, which extended as far south as Boca Raton and north to Juno Beach.

It was only after they had finished eating and were dawdling over second cups of coffee that he directed the conversation to her reason for being there. Without any hesitation, he expressed his pessimism about her being able to accomplish her mission.

"Sorry to be so discouraging," he said sympathetically, noting her downcast features, "but I'm just being brutally honest with you. These people are not the *nouveaux riches* who are more apt to be cooperative with the media. You're talking about families who've been spectacularly rich for generations. Even though times have changed since the early part of this century, some of the old estates along Ocean Boulevard still have a guard at the gate and a whole army of servants maintaining the place. The biggest difference between now and fifty or sixty years ago is that quite a number of places are permanent homes rather than just wintering places, thanks to air-conditioning."

"There's got to be a way to get on the inside," Kelly said doggedly, the obvious solution foremost in her mind. "Maybe I could get a job as a maid or something."

His eyes gleamed with sardonic skepticism as they swept the pale shimmer of her hair, rested on her cameo features and then slid briefly down the upper portion of her figure visible to his gaze. "Oh, sure," he murmured wryly.

"I could make myself look plain," she protested, faintly embarrassed as well as flattered by the frank admiration of his assessment. "The problem will be finding out who might need a domestic worker and then figuring out how to make an application. I'm sure these people don't work through the county employment agency."

"Hardly," he agreed ironically. "Their security investigation would rival the U.S. government's."

"Oh, dear, I hadn't thought about that possibility," Kelly admitted ruefully, her spirits sinking lower every second. She was suddenly overcome by travel fatigue, which was worsened by the realization that this whole trip was probably nothing more than a wild-goose chase.

The man across the table seemed to take pity on her. As if wrestling with his better judgment, he hesitated and then overrode his own reluctance. "Tell you what. Why don't you just go to bed tonight and sleep on it. Tomorrow morning I'll check around and see what I can come up with. We can have lunch together and I'll let you know if I've been able to pick up anything through the grapevine."

On that note she left the restaurant, shoulders sagging, and returned to the small bungalow-style motel. Located on the outskirts of West Palm Beach away from the expensive luxury hotels, its accommodations were sparsely adequate and clean. In her present mood of self-pity, she almost would have preferred something less comfortable.

The next morning she awoke restored to her normal

energetic self. Stretching lazily, she lay in bed a few extra minutes going over in careful detail the conversation with Philip Lawson the previous night. In a way, she was grateful to him for being so frank. Coming up against the blank wall of his pessimism was a test to her determination.

She dressed in casual lightweight slacks and a sleeveless top, anticipating the tropical warmth of the sun beaming down outside. With any luck at all she would return home to New Orleans with a suntan that would be the envy of the station.

Two hours later she stared at Philip Lawson in amazement, unaware that her mouth hung open. He had just divulged to her his findings of the morning. Lady Jane Wessen, a dowager who owned one of the most opulent of the old mansions designed by the eccentric architect Addison Mizner, had just fired her personal secretary. From what Philip had been able to glean from his contacts, the old woman's main dissatisfaction with the unfortunate secretary was her attractive appearance and ambitions to make a marital contact among Lady Wessen's social circle.

"Apparently said secretary was a well-born young woman herself but poor, her family having fallen upon bad times—perfect stereotype of the secretary-companion, from the sounds of it. It would be the ideal situation for you, if you could land it. You'd be right in the middle of the *crème de la crème*—the Everglades Club, the Bath and Tennis Club, the whole works."

Something surprisingly akin to bitterness flickered briefly in Philip's eyes before the customary detachment settled in place again. "The Smith-Boyd Agency, a very old, snobbish firm, handles Lady Wessen's staff applications and screens them down to the most suitable ones, which she herself then interviews. Too bad—" He sighed ruefully.

Kelly knew he was thinking that she wasn't in the least suitable, but her mind was racing ahead. This was

18

it! Her perfect opportunity! "So what Lady Wessen ideally wants in a secretary is someone so physically plain no man will give her more than a passing glance, someone who types and does the usual secretary-type things and, most importantly, *knows her place.*"

"In a nutshell, you might say." Respect for the succinctness of her grasp of the situation gleamed in Philip's eyes.

"Thanks, Philip." The fervor in her voice portrayed an excitement that drew a curious expression across his bored features. "You've saved the day. No—no, don't say it!" She stopped him with an uplifted hand. "I'm going to get that job. You're looking at Lady Jane Wessen's new secretary." Her voice changed to a flat smug tone. "The good Lord knew what he was doing when he made all kinds. As for me, I wouldn't change places with a Rockefeller."

"You know something, Kelly. You just might pull it off," he said with grudging admiration. "If you can figure out some kind of way to hide that face and figure, you just might do it."

At that moment, the possibility of Kelly's being able to hide her beauty seemed particularly ludicrous. Her lips curved in a wide smile that revealed even white teeth, her brown eyes fairly sparkled with exhilaration and her blond hair fell from an off-center part to her shoulders in startling contrast to her dark eyes and lashes.

She could hardly restrain her impatience to get started at once implementing her plan. She agreed to have dinner with him that night in her disguise. "I'll pay," she insisted. "After all, I'll be able to afford it with my new salary."

"Don't count on it," he countered dryly. "Even if you get the job—rich doesn't mean generous, you know." The rancor in his tone made little impression on her at the time.

Leaving Philip, she drove to a huge shopping mall in

West Palm Beach, where she spent several hours in the careful selection of the items she needed. Until she actually was assured of getting the job, she would purchase only what she needed for the interview with the agency and then, hopefully, with Lady Wessen herself.

According to what Philip had said, Lady Wessen's ten-acre estate included not just an olympic size swimming pool but tennis courts and a long private stretch on the Atlantic Ocean. This job was shaping up into the opportunity of a lifetime, even without the assignment. The more she thought of the potential of the feature she planned to do, the more she was sure it was material for national syndication as well as for her own local station.

One tiny worry nudged at the back of her mind. What would Mom and Dad think of what she was planning to do? Knowing them, they would probably think it was dishonest to pretend to be something you weren't. She would worry about what to tell her parents *after* she definitely got the job. Maybe it would be better not to tell them the truth, since it would only cause them needless concern. After all, she wouldn't even consider going through the deception if it meant harm to the people involved.

With that salve applied to her conscience, Kelly thrust aside her misgivings and became absorbed in the task of transforming herself into another person. It was wonderful fun, much like the childhood game of dressing up in the cast-off clothes of adults. And the final result was infinitely satisfying. Could that dowdy woman in the mirror actually be herself?

She had parted her hair down the middle and fastened it with a plain tortoiseshell barrette at the nape of the neck. Her clear flawless complexion was covered with a gray liquid makeup which had a strangely dulling effect on the bright tint of her hair. Otherwise she wore no makeup. Eyeglasses with dark heavy frames partially hid the usual effect of petal-soft brown eyes.

Her shirtwaist dress of drab gray and beige was a size too large. The shoes were not cheap but were the styleless "sensible" oxfords one immediately and unkindly associates with a spinster schoolteacher or librarian. The unremarkable tan color and low squat heels did nothing to highlight Kelly's shapely legs.

Her confidence surged to new heights when she confronted Philip at the restaurant where they had arranged to meet. "I can't believe it," he exclaimed, and looked around in feigned concern. "I just hope nobody I know sees me with this poor frumpish creature. My reputation as a womanizer will be ruined!"

By the end of the evening, having been subjected to the new Kelly, a person of smug opinions and definite class consciousness, Philip was sold on her chances for success. Her disguise wavered only when the check was delivered to their table and he handed it to her with a flourish.

"Here. You pay. Now that you'll be a working-woman."

She put back her head and laughed in an abandoned fashion incongruously out of character with her staid appearance. "Can you imagine?" she managed to choke out. "I'll have to have a whole wardrobe like this!"

Chapter Three

Consulting the map of Palm Beach County she had purchased at a bookstore in the shopping mall the previous day, Kelly easily located the building which housed the agency, a discreet white frame building with a black-lettered sign announcing *Smith-Boyd Agency*. Her appointment wasn't until eleven o'clock, giving her ample time to drive around Palm Beach, which in actuality resembled a long narrow island separated from the mainland by Lake Worth, named after the general who subdued hostile Indians in the area during the previous century.

In spite of everything she had been told to expect, the impact of the island's opulence was overwhelming. Royal Palm Way lived up to its name, lined by magnificent towering palm trees which imparted a sense of majesty that made Kelly feel not only insignificant but intrusive as well in her small Volkswagen. It was a street designed for a royal procession, not just ordinary traffic.

Just as impressive in its own way was Worth Avenue, a pristine little street in the business area several blocks south of Royal Palm Way. Small shops with brightly striped awnings shading the immaculate sidewalks sported names one expected to find in New York City, not southern Florida—Saks Fifth Avenue, Bonwit Teller, Cartier, and Schwarz.

Driving the length of Ocean Boulevard, she was in danger of losing her nerve, so awed was she by the tantalizing glimpses of palatial mansions behind high protective walls. Some of them looked like Moorish castles out of another century, their towers and turrets crowned by red tile roofs. Vistas of exquisitely groomed grounds beyond lacy iron gates contributed to the all-pervasive aura of fabulous wealth.

Never before had Kelly experienced such an acute sense of social inferiority as she viewed the twin towers of the prestigious old hotel The Breakers. Like an old aristocrat awaiting carefully chosen guests, it presided at the edge of the Atlantic Ocean, and only those with the credentials of great wealth could approach it along a stately drive, flanked by lawns flawlessly landscaped and tended.

Feeling more and more all the time like an alien trespassing on foreign territory, she returned to the agency for her interview. With a self-mocking little grimace, she reflected that it shouldn't be too difficult to assume an attitude of humility, and then chided herself for being so impressionable.

Still, the tour of the island had shaken her confidence in her ability to carry off the deception, for in truth she was intimidated at the prospect of venturing inside those high walls she saw everywhere. No longer, though, did she harbor the slightest compunction about what she planned to do. It was difficult to think of this exclusive colony of pampered, insular people as ordinary humans. No, she wouldn't experience the slightest guilt about invading their closely guarded privacy.

Just as she strode up the walk leading to the white-painted door, an incident occurred which helped to restore her depleted self-confidence and flagging sense of purpose. A young man whose erect bearing and impeccable gray suit lent him an air of self-importance came through the door, trotted briskly down the steps and proceeded past Kelly without so much as a nod or a glance. While not a conceited girl, she was so accustomed to appraising looks from men of all ages and occupations that it came as a surprise to be so totally ignored.

Suddenly it dawned upon her that the disguise had just passed the first real test. She was neither attractive nor ugly enough to merit a glance! With renewed confidence she squared her shoulders and marched through the door and into the foyer, ready to face and vanquish the enemy.

Almost two hours later, iron and brass filigreed gates clicked ominously shut behind her, and Kelly was driving along the curving driveway of Casa de Fresa toward her confrontation with Lady Jane Wessen. Her apprehension dissolved, replaced by openmouthed awe as she stared unbelievingly at the grounds stretching away on each side. She might have likened the landscaped gardens to those of a royal park surrounding a monarch's castle had she ever had the opportunity to see the authentic models. Marble statuary and benches, lovely fountains and lush tropical foliage created an overall effect that took her breath away.

Then, without warning, she rounded a sharp curve and came upon the house itself. Looking centuries old rather than a mere sixty years, the sand-tone stuccoed walls were almost hidden behind the tropical vines. On either side was a square tower, crowned with reddish-brown Spanish tiles as were all the complex angles of the roof. The windows and doors were narrow, and arched like those in a Gothic cathedral.

Her most immediate consideration was a very practi-

cal one. Was she expected to go to a side entrance?
Dare she walk right up to the enormous arched doors at
the imposing entrance? The thought was daunting, but
fortunately her sense of humor was working overtime
at the sheer unreality of her present situation. Reflecting wryly that it was positively advantageous that her
role called for a strong belief in a social caste system,
she clutched her sensible tan handbag, which matched
her sensible tan shoes, and marched up to the grand
portals.

After what seemed an interminable wait, the door
was opened by a man who looked incredibly like a
butler in an Agatha Christie mystery novel. Kelly
smothered a nervous urge to giggle as she stepped
inside and found herself in a huge vaulted hall complete
with silver suits of armor and wall lamps shaped like
medieval sconces. Both floor and walls were rough-
hewn stone and liberally covered with beautiful Oriental rugs and tapestries. Even Kelly's untrained eye
discerned the wide variety of design and color, some
instinct telling her that here was a vast fortune in
antique weaving in just one room.

The butler cleared his throat and said, "This way,
miss, if you please," in the condescending manner
perfect for his calling, and Kelly was seized with an
insane urge to do or say something outrageous to test
his composure. Following him across an endless expanse of stone floor, she knew she should be nervous at
the prospect of the interview facing her. But somehow
the whole experience was too much like a tour through
Disney World for her to take it seriously.

The threat of hysteria subsided when she entered a
room considerably more conventional than the medieval hall. There was time for only a quick look around at
stiffly formal furnishings in what appeared to be a
sitting room, its generous size no doubt considered
small in this house. The furniture was Louis XV, the
dark polished wood ornately carved and the upholstery

a stiff satin brocade. In one corner was a large black lacquer secretary, lavishly emblazoned with gold dragons.

The woman facing Kelly across the room looked as if her spine conformed with ease to the ramrod straightness of the chair in which she sat. Eyes like hard blue marbles raked Kelly from head to toe and back to head.

"Miss Lindsay, I presume. Sit down over there." She made a peremptory motion toward a chair as elegant and uninviting as the one in which she sat.

This is too much, Kelly reflected to herself unbelievingly. Lady Jane Wessen was as true to the stereotype of *grande dame* as the haughty man had been to the cinema conception of a butler. The older woman appeared to be in her sixties and had an imperious air worthy of a queen. Her silver-gray hair was swept up to the top of her head, where it formed perfect, stiff curls that surely couldn't budge even in hurricane-force winds. Diamonds blazed in her earlobes, and heavily veined hands seemed weighted down with sumptuous jewels.

It had been Kelly's observation that nearly all women age in one of two ways. Some become softly rounded, like one imagines a storybook grandmother to look, while others take on a rigid, bony appearance, as if the flesh has all melted away under the skin. Lady Jane Wessen fit into the latter of the two categories. Her pale-blue linen suit seemed to touch her angular frame only at the narrow shoulders.

Lady Wessen asked essentially the same questions as the man at the agency, and she seemed satisfied with the answers. Kelly gave the fictional name of a lady from New Orleans with whom she had been traveling as a secretary-companion. The job had been terminated by Kelly herself just weeks ago in Florida when the lady's son had made improper sexual advances toward her. Kelly regretted that she did not know the present whereabouts of her former employer, as she traveled about from place to place ceaselessly.

At the point in the interview when Kelly was sketching in an account of her educational background, she was forced to pause when a small boy entered the room and stood quietly waiting to be recognized.

"Yes, Jamie, what do you want?" Lady Wessen's voice held a trace of irritation at the interruption.

"Excuse me, Grandmother. May I swim in the pool? I promise I'll be very careful."

Kelly examined him curiously. What a very solemn little boy; he was standing there, oddly composed and formal for one so young. Mentally she compared him with her own self and her younger brother and sisters at that age, which she estimated to be about six or seven.

"You know you can't swim in the pool unsupervised, Jamie, and Eloise has the afternoon off. You may play with your toys in the nursery or you may play outside as long as you stay away from the pool and don't go near the ocean. Now run along."

Apparently unmoved by the droop of small features, Lady Wessen transferred her attention back to Kelly. Her grandson had been clearly dismissed. Before leaving the room as quietly as he had entered, he gave Kelly a look that shook her with its total lack of normal curiosity. His dark eyes had a resignation startling in one so young, and she was oddly disturbed by the brief interruption.

"Miss Lindsay, how would you feel if fate had reversed our roles and *you* were mistress of Casa de Fresa and *I* were applying for a secretary's position?"

The final question Lady Wessen directed at Kelly evoked a fleeting image of the small, taciturn boy. The older woman would have been startled by the soft velvety beauty of the dark eyes behind the unflattering spectacles. For a moment, Kelly could see the rambling old house in which she had grown up, the wide screened veranda and large yard more than ample for the childish exploits conceived and executed by herself and her friends. She thought of her loving, scatter-brained mother, coping in her own way with rearing seven children and yet managing to spend productive hours at the typewriter composing the many articles and short stories that not only contributed to the family coffers but earned her a modest reputation among publishers of women's and family magazines. She could see her father as he bent over the neat rows of his large vegetable garden and performed chores around the house many men would consider demeaning women's work.

"Lady Wessen, I wouldn't trade places with you for anything in the world," Kelly replied with conviction, speaking directly from her heart without a thought to the role she was playing.

"I see."

The hard blue eyes showed satisfaction with the answer. "I hadn't expected to find anyone so quickly. Normally I consult with my son on these matters, but at the moment he is away. If the salary and conditions of employment meet with your satisfaction, the position is yours."

She mentioned a sum Kelly found neither generous nor miserly, remembering privately Philip's comment about the rich not always being generous.

"The work is not onerous," Lady Wessen continued, "primarily my correspondence, both business and personal. You will also run errands for me, do small shopping chores, generally be at my beck and call. It's nothing I couldn't do myself." Her condescending tone made it clear that one in her position didn't have to do *anything* she didn't choose to do.

Careful not to appear too eager, Kelly stated her satisfaction with the salary and the responsibilities Lady Wessen had outlined. After explaining the necessity for taking care of some personal business, she agreed to return the following day. Part of her remuneration would be food and lodging, a circumstance that delighted her no end, since it would undoubtedly allow her to nose around the estate and take pictures during her leisure time. She was depending upon Lady Wessen's involvement in innumerable social activities.

There was no time to waste now. Kelly spent the remainder of the afternoon and the following morning shopping for the necessary clothing and accessories. She kept her purchases to a minimum, estimating that she could get the material she needed in a few weeks, a month at the outside.

To her surprise, Lady Wessen herself was present to greet Kelly and show her around Casa de Fresa when she arrived during the afternoon. Kelly's astonishment must have shown clearly on her face when it was revealed to her that the stairs leading to the upper stories of the two wings flanking the central portion of the house were located in the two towers on either side. The architect—the eccentric Addison Mizner, who was responsible for transforming this small tropical island into a medieval anomaly—had not seen fit to place a stairway in the huge central hall.

"Apparently he maintained that an inside staircase would destroy the whole effect he was creating," Lady Wessen explained with what looked surprisingly like a glint of humor in the hard blue eyes at the dumbfounded expression on Kelly's face. "I've been tempted many times to install an elevator, but laziness is the malady that's undermining this whole country. Walking up a few stairs never hurt anyone. When I get too old to get up to my apartment on my own steam, perhaps I'll move into one of those dreadful condominiums." She shuddered with distaste.

Leading Kelly past arched doors with hinges and latch fittings of crude black iron, she stopped finally to push one open. "This is your room. My rooms and those of my grandson are also on this floor. The south wing is seldom used anymore."

Kelly struggled to conceal her astonishment as she stood just inside the room indicated as her own and gazed about her. The room was enormous. One-half was furnished as a sitting area and the other half as a bedroom. All the furniture was eighteenth-century French and undoubtedly very fine and costly, even to her untrained eye. The bed, in particular, caught her attention, a towering canopied affair with intricately carved woodwork and a bedspread with matching draperies of lustrous satin. How in the world would she ever be able to sleep in that!

There was a matching *armoire* and highboy, an ornate little dressing table with a gilt-framed mirror, delicately carved tables and chests, a stiffly graceful sofa and two chairs, and silk-shaded lamps. It was more than enough furniture to fill Kelly's apartment in New Orleans, and yet the room did not seem in the least crowded.

"Apparently you were expecting a monk's cell furnished with a cot and washbasin," reflected Lady Wessen with a wry humor that clashed with Kelly's whole concept of her employer's personality.

"This is very nice, Lady Wessen." Remembering her role, Kelly laced her voice and manner with a slight hint of disapproval at such extravagant luxury. Her curiosity propelled her over to one of the tall arched windows draped in heavy satin with coarse lace tiebacks. "Ah!" She sucked in her breath at the magnificent view. Her room overlooked the rear grounds of the estate and the private ocean beach. "How beautiful," she murmured, forgetfully lapsing into her own personality.

"Come along now, and I'll show you the bathroom, which you will have to yourself. Then we'll go rather quickly through the remainder of the house so that you'll be able to find your way around." Lady Wessen was once again her imperious self with no time to be bothered with the enthusiasms of a mere secretary. Kelly was sure she must have imagined that brief glint of humor which made the older woman almost likable for a few moments.

She followed her employer and mentally made notes of the location of her apartment and that of her grandson, which included the nursery and the room of the woman Eloise, who looked after him. During the tour of the downstairs central portion of the house, she met Sanford, the butler, and his wife, Lucille, the cook, a dour little woman who couldn't have weighed more than ninety pounds. Besides Kelly, these two and Eloise were the only other live-in employees. The servants who cleaned the house and the gardeners came during the day and left when their work was completed.

Kelly felt as if she had just walked through a museum by the time the brisk tour ended. Her eyes had seen more than her dazed mind could record and they hadn't even bothered to enter the south wing. For the first time, she wished she knew something about antiques and art. Her small-town background had not trained her to identify the abundance of priceless articles she saw everywhere—porcelain vases and figurines, exquisite clocks and the innumerable rugs and tapestries, some of which were obviously fragments of larger creations. She knew instinctively that this collection of woven articles was extensive, and Lady Wessen confirmed that opinion when she made casual mention of the fact that hers was probably the largest and most comprehensive private collection of Oriental rugs in the United States.

Kelly resolved to pursue that subject further at the first opportunity. It might be just the slant she was looking for in her feature.

"You may explore the grounds at your leisure," Lady Wessen announced, breaking into Kelly's reflections.

"Feel free to swim in the pool when it is not in use." Her tone was that of someone bestowing an enormous favor.

"For the time being, you will eat your meals with Sanford and Lucille. Now I really must dress for a dinner engagement. If you have no pressing questions, I will expect you to be ready to begin work at nine o'clock in the morning."

Swallowing the bile in her throat, Kelly managed to incline her head submissively. There was so much she had neglected to consider such as where and with whom she would eat her meals. It wasn't that she minded in the least sitting down with Lady Wessen's servants, but her employer's supercilious manner was offensive. Kelly wondered only fleetingly why she had said "for the time being," dismissing the thought as she went to find Lucille and learn the schedule for meals.

The evening meal turned out to be an almost elegant affair, served not in the kitchen as she had expected, but in the servants' dining room, which adjoined the kitchen. Eloise was taking her meal with her young charge and was not present, leaving Kelly with Sanford and Lucille.

If she had expected to be readily accepted by her fellow workers, she was sadly mistaken. Perhaps they were afraid of letting down their guard too quickly with a stranger who might reveal their confidences to the lady of the house. Conversation was stilted, and Kelly finally gave up the attempt to elicit information from the taciturn couple and concentrated instead on the excellent meal. If it was any indication of the typical servants' fare, she would have to watch her calorie intake during this job.

The next few days passed without presenting any difficulties in the fulfillment of her duties. The actual work she performed could have been done in one or two hours of the day, at most. But Lady Jane, as all her employees called her, seemed to draw out each task as long as possible. At first Kelly wondered if the older woman wasn't as sharp as she had appeared that first day. Then gradually the realization dawned that her employer was simply filling the empty hours.

Kelly had envisioned the aristocratic woman as dashing from one social invitation to another in her chauffeur-driven vintage limousine, when in actuality she was less than enthusiastic about the few functions she chose to attend. She had just dictated a note of acceptance to a large fashion-show luncheon at the Everglades Club when Kelly commented, "Sounds like fun."

Lady Jane smiled with a hint of weariness. "Just a bunch of idle women who justify their existence by raising money for charity."

A week passed since she had first come to Casa de Fresa, and finally she got the opportunity to explore the grounds on her own. Lady Jane would be gone the entire afternoon, and Kelly looked forward to the hours of leisure with keen anticipation.

Abandoning part of her usual disguise, she donned a pair of old jeans, a shirt and canvas sneakers. The temptation was strong to free her hair and cast aside the heavy spectacles. But she resisted, deciding it was too risky to wander around the estate looking like her real self. A chance encounter with one of the servants might arouse their curiosity.

So with a sigh of resignation, recognizing with surprise how tired she was already of her frumpish disguise, she put on the dark-rimmed eyeglasses, slung the strap of her camera over one shoulder and set off on her exploration.

She spent some time photographing the huge tiled terrace with its planters of blooming shrubs and profusion of lovely wicker patio furniture. Some distance away was an amoeba-shaped swimming pool, a brilliant splash of turquoise in the midst of lounge chairs and tables shaded by striped umbrellas.

Beyond the swimming pool, perfect green lawns dotted with palm trees extended down to the pristine whiteness of the sandy beach. Beyond that was the infinity of the ocean, today a tranquil blue.

Kelly headed off to the right, past the modern tennis courts, and entered a garden so densely planted with azaleas, oleanders and numerous varieties of other plants that the view of the ocean was obstructed. Worn pathways meandered and sometimes crossed one another. Nestled among the lush shrubbery were occasional little nooks with marble benches beside the cool fountains and man-made brooks.

Then unexpectedly the path she was following merged with what appeared to be a driveway. Her spirit of adventure increased as she followed it until it came to a small cottage painted a pale green so that it almost blended with the trees and dense foliage surrounding it. A deep silence, disturbed only by the husky whisper of the surf, told her no one was near.

Surmising that she was looking at the back of the cottage, Kelly followed a brick path around the side that led to the beachfront. A tiny lawn ended abruptly at a line of heavy creosoted timbers which formed a protective bulkhead between the cottage and the encroachment of the ocean at high tide.

Steps made of the same rude timbers as the bulkhead led steeply down to the beach, and from the telltale marbling of the sand she knew that at certain times one could sit on the veranda and watch the mighty ocean lick at the bottom steps. The thought made her shiver with a mixture of apprehension and pleasure.

Following a strong impulse, she walked up the simple brick steps to the veranda and studied the smooth green panels of the door a few seconds before reaching out tentatively for the polished brass doorknob. It turned easily under her hand! She couldn't resist looking inside.

"Well, I'll be . . ." she murmured in astonishment,

stepping through the door into a sitting room furnished in ultramodern decor: low couches in rich brown leather, glass-topped tables and spherical lamps with chrome bases. A beautiful rug of bold geometric design in black, brown and white covered the center of the floor, and enormous unframed modern paintings dominated the walls. Vibrant yellows and oranges seemed to leap off the wall at Kelly. Woven wood roman shades were pulled as high as they could go, leaving the windows bare to admit natural light.

The room pulsed with life. Nothing could be in more startling contrast to Casa de Fresa.

Dumbfounded and intrigued, Kelly wandered from room to room, continually charmed by the utility and design in the furnishings. The choice of bright colors managed to alleviate the bleakness she sometimes found objectionable in contemporary decorating.

Later she would wonder that something had not alerted her to the presence of another person. She must have been too engrossed in her exploration to hear the approach of an automobile or footsteps. Somehow it was doubly embarrassing to be discovered in the bedroom, where she was admiring the low king-size bed, the plush spread in bold diagonal stripes of cranberry and navy folded back to reveal silk sheets and pillowcases in the same rich colors. The built-in headboard contained reading lights, book shelves and compartments for clock and radio.

"Would you care to sample its pleasures before I call the police?"

Kelly whirled around, to stare at the source of that deep, contemptuous male voice. As she did so, the strap of her camera slipped, making it necessary for her to grab it before the expensive instrument crashed to the floor. She stood frozen in that position, one arm across her chest with the hand clutching the strap on her shoulder.

The tall man leaning against the doorjamb noted the

35

movement with hard blue eyes narrowed with anger. His eyes raked her form and then returned to rest on the black leather case of her camera, which had been her parents' college-graduation present and was the pride of her possessions.

"You'd do well to hang on to that. I've a good mind to throw it in the ocean." As if he planned to enact the insolent threat, the man straightened, and Kelly took one frightened step backward. Her knees came up against the edge of the bed, and without warning buckled underneath her, causing her to drop inelegantly onto the lush velvet of the spread.

"You can't do that! It's mine. You have no right," she objected fiercely, clutching the camera with both hands as he came a step nearer. She stared up into deeply tanned masculine features taut with anger. The strong mouth twisted in a mocking sneer.

"And this is mine," he countered, raising a hand as brown as his face to indicate their surroundings. "Nor do you have any *right* to be here."

He was towering over her now, and she feared at any moment he would rip the camera from her hands and carry out his intention to destroy it. Now was no time to cling to pride or personal dignity.

"Please! I had no intention of trespassing. This cottage *is* on Lady Jane's property, isn't it? And she said I could look around anywhere I wanted . . ."

Her words, while causing him to hesitate, increased his barely controlled fury. "I've got to give you credit for gall. Like the rest of your breed, you'd risk life and limb for a story and a few photographs."

This man, whoever he was, believed her to be a reporter sneaking around the estate. But who was he? From the expensive tailoring of his slacks and shirt and the autocratic bearing, he obviously wasn't a workman.

"You're going to have to think faster than that if you plan to get ahead in the world of journalistic spying." The cutting sarcasm reminded her she still hadn't explained who she was, or more to the point, who she was *supposed* to be.

At the moment she wished she had the benefit of one of the dowdy outfits she had purchased especially for her secretary's role. It was difficult to project dignity attired as she was, but she rose stiffly to her feet, forcing him to step back unless he wanted her nose pressed against his chest, and he obviously didn't.

"Allow me to introduce myself," she announced in the smug "I know my place" tone. "I am Miss Lindsay, Lady Jane Wessen's secretary, and *who,* may I ask, are *you?*"

The tall man folded his arms across his broad chest and stood in a stance that drew attention to his long muscular legs beneath the soft tan fabric of his slacks. Kelly resisted the urge to squirm beneath the scrutiny of his sardonic blue eyes, which swept her from head to toe.

"The latest sacrificial offering, eh? *Ma mère* isn't taking any chances this time." The cryptic words, delivered in a mocking tone, confused Kelly and alerted her to the startling fact that she had apparently wandered right into the personal quarters of Lady Jane's son, the one who had not been available to give his opinion of hiring Kelly since he was away at the time of the interview. What rotten luck to have him walk in on her like this! She only hoped she hadn't blown her disguise in those minutes before she remembered to turn on the role.

"Please accept my apology for blundering into your private quarters," she offered with icy formality. "Lady Jane is away all afternoon, and at her invitation I am taking advantage of the opportunity to look around the grounds. Quite by accident I happened upon this cottage and—"

"Just like Goldilocks, couldn't resist looking inside?" The teeth revealed by the mocking smile were very white against the deep tan of his face. Quite involuntarily, Kelly realized that Lady Jane's son, though hostile, was definitely a virile, attractive man. Was he the reason his mother fired her former secretary and determined to hire someone unattractive?

"Perhaps you have a telephone?" She looked around the room with a hint of disapproval. "You can call the main house and talk to either Sanford or Lucille."

"I have a better idea, er—" He groped for her name.

"Miss Lindsay," she supplied crisply, and wondered at the slight quirk of his mouth.

"Of course, *Miss Lindsay*. Why don't you leave that expensive-looking camera with me? If you are who you say you are, you'll get it back this evening. May I assume you will inform Lady Jane of my arrival when she returns home?"

Every instinct resisted the idea of relinquishing the prized camera, but it seemed the prudent thing to do under the circumstances. After all, she would get it back.

"Very well, Mr.—er—Wessen?" She raised her eyebrows inquiringly.

"Mathison. Blair Mathison." He bowed stiffly from the waist, a wicked gleam in the blue eyes.

About to hand over the camera, Kelly hesitated at the name. If he were indeed Lady Jane's son, would he not have the same surname? Suddenly overcome by the complexities of the situation into which she had unwittingly involved herself, she thrust the camera in his proffered hand, nodded curtly and summoned as much dignity in leaving the room as one can manage dressed in old jeans and canvas sneakers. Thank God she had worn the spectacles and retained the severe hairstyle!

Shoulders and chin held high, she marched along the brick walk to the driveway, resisting the urge to break into a run. A ridiculous prickling all along the back of her ramrod figure made her wonder if she were being watched from a window in the cottage, but she dared not hazard a quick look over her shoulder. Only after she had gained the safety of one of the paths inside the dense foliage did she relax.

The afternoon was far from over, but the recent experience had shaken her so severely that all she wanted to do was to return immediately to the safety of her own room. Why did this have to happen just when she was beginning to feel confident of the success of her daring imposture? Instinct told her Blair Mathison was no fool, and she feared the penetrating scrutiny of those shrewd blue eyes.

She had no pictures yet of the interior of the mansion or of Lady Jane. She had planned to cultivate an image of herself as an amateur photographer, thereby quieting any suspicions her picture-taking might arouse. Eventually she hoped to get shots of Lady Jane entertaining friends, of the servants at work and of Jamie, the heir-apparent to all this magnificence. But if Blair Mathison uncovered her real identity, she would be lucky to get her camera back, *without* the film she had shot today. Even though the insight gained during the past week was a journalist's dream, without pictures the story would not be of use to Stan Curtis.

What a mess! she reflected drearily, dragging herself up the steps to her bedroom.

Chapter Four

"He must have been furious, thinking a reporter had sneaked into his beloved cottage! *I* wouldn't go myself, uninvited. And Blair places news reporters at the top of his list of despicable and worthless people."

Lady Jane had been amused by Kelly's carefully slanted account of her unpleasant experience that afternoon. After hours of pondering, she had decided to get her version in first, and in all modesty she had to applaud herself for a superb acting performance. At one point her lip had trembled in hurt indignation over the harsh way she had been treated by the stranger who had discovered her looking around the cottage that, after all, *was* unlocked.

"Don't worry about a thing, dear. I'll smooth this over with Blair. He is inclined to be a bit of a bully at times. Take my advice and don't ever have just one child."

Kelly didn't know whether to be most astounded at the friendly tone of voice and the endearment or the nature of the advice. Surely Lady Jane didn't think any man would want to *marry* someone so unprepossessing as her secretary?

The mystery of Blair Mathison's name had been solved by Lady Jane, who explained that she had been married three times—very happily, she interposed. Her second husband was the father of her son, her only child. Blair's grandfather had built Casa de Fresa as a wintering home used primarily for entertaining a huge circle of friends, including many titled dignitaries.

Discretion forbade Kelly's asking about the circumstances leading to Lady Jane's being in charge of the upbringing of her grandson. It wasn't until she met Jamie's father that her curiosity about the boy's mother was whetted. Jamie must look like her, Kelly reflected, failing to detect any likeness of the diminutive dark-eyed boy to the tall assured man she had encountered that afternoon.

The days following Blair Mathison's return to Casa de Fresa precipitated little change in Kelly's schedule other than to give her more free time. To her mingled relief and disappointment, she seldom saw him. But Lady Jane was more willing to accept invitations as long as her son was available to escort her.

Precisely a week after the day Kelly had inadvertently wandered into the cottage, she found herself with an entire day to herself. Lady Jane would not return until the afternoon, and then only to dress for a dinner and depart again. Her son was to accompany her to the social functions. She advised Kelly to take advantage of the time as she saw fit, reminding her that the pool and terrace and the entire beach would be hers to use.

Following Kelly's abrasive encounter with her son, the older woman had been surprisingly human. Kelly forced herself to harden her natural inclination toward empathy. She just couldn't afford to get involved with her employer. She *had* to keep an emotional distance in order to get her job done.

After Lady Jane had departed, decked out in pale-blue linen and sumptuous pearls, Kelly got to work taking interior shots of the house, including several superb ones of Lucille and Sanford, who no longer seemed quite so standoffish as they had been the first few days.

Sanford was busy polishing silver, standing behind a table loaded with elaborate serving trays, tureens, bowls, goblets and candleholders. Kelly couldn't have asked for a better picture to display the lavish wealth of a Palm Beach household. The expression on Sanford's face was perfect, a bored ho-hum look that clearly indicated this was an every-day routine for the butler in Lady Jane's employ.

After using up all the film she had, she decided to drive into West Palm Beach and leave it to be developed. On impulse she telephoned Philip Lawson, who sounded delighted to hear from her and insisted she have lunch with him. He was leaving town that afternoon on business but would be gone only a couple of days. They arranged a meeting place.

She returned to Casa de Fresa and realized that there was still time for a walk along the beach before Lady Jane returned. The idea appealed so strongly that she changed into a plain brown one-piece bathing suit. Its old-fashioned pleated skirt couldn't totally disguise the slender shape of her figure. Still she felt safe from the eyes of her employer and her arrogant son.

Gathering up a canvas tote bag, she moved over to close the open doors of the tall *armoire* and caught sight of herself in one of the long mirrors lining the doors. With a brown cover-up over her prim suit, her feet in brown straw sandals, hair drawn back in the barrette and dark-rimmed glasses in place, she was unrecognizable to herself, even after two weeks. With a shudder of revulsion, she resisted the impulse to throw aside the clumsy eyeglasses and shake her hair free. Assuming a personality so alien to her own was far more taxing than she had expected.

Instead of strolling across the immense lawns down to the ocean, in full sight of the house, she took a path off to the left past the sprawling bulk of the huge garage. Not pausing to admire the secluded little resting places with intricately sculpted marble seats and fountains, she headed directly toward the tantalizing sounds and scent of the ocean.

Exhilaration welled up as she found herself finally on the beach. She flung down the canvas tote, kicked off the sandals and stripped off the cover-up. Standing like a young goddess of nature with face upturned to the vast blue sky, she extended her arms as if to welcome the approach of the tide.

With a guttural sound in her throat, she succumbed to the sheer necessity of discarding the unneeded eyeglasses and, with fingers trembling with excitement, unfastened the hated barrette. What harm would it do? She would stay out of sight of the house and return before Lady Jane was due back.

She was so involved with her sensuous enjoyment of running barefoot along the sand, the ocean breeze fanning her spun white-gold hair, that she didn't at first see the small figure of a child far down the beach. With a surprise she realized it was Jamie!

"Oh, darn!" she muttered heartbrokenly, and slowed to a sedate walk, knowing that Eloise must be around somewhere, too. The child was not allowed on the beach alone. The most Kelly could hope was that the nursemaid had been too busy observing her small charge to notice Kelly's abandoned progress along the curling edge of the ocean.

Her first inclination was to turn around and head the other way. But that would take her in full sight of the main house and eventually to the small green cottage, which was definitely off limits to her. Besides, Jamie had obviously already spotted her, and something defiant in the set of the small head and shoulders aroused Kelly's curiosity. Eloise still was not in sight. Was it possible the boy had defied his grandmother and come down to the ocean alone?

He stood his ground, watching her. When she got closer, she could read the resentment in the dark eyes, the tenseness in the slight body. Seven years old and already he had the manner of an aristocrat, she reflected to herself with inward irony.

"Hi, Jamie. Out for a walk?" she greeted cheerfully.

"Are you going to tell them?" he demanded without polite preamble.

With the benefit of experience with three younger siblings, she knew it was pointless to pretend ignorance. Children, like animals, possessed a disconcerting ability to detect insincerity.

"Do you think I should?" she countered, dropping to sit on the sand a short distance from him, thereby bringing her eyes closer to a level with his own.

"It's really none of your business," he replied curtly.

Awed in spite of herself by his implacable poise, she had to concede his logic. Her own younger sisters and brother at his age would have been wailing for mercy and begging not to be given away, promising everything under the sun in exchange for a reprieve.

"I suppose you're right," she agreed thoughtfully. "As long as I'm here, you're actually in the company of an adult, as your grandmother insists. What would you say to a bargain?"

Something about the way the sensitive lips curled into a sneer reminded Kelly fleetingly of his father. The expression said more than words what he thought of negotiating with her, but he said skeptically, "A bargain?"

"You promise not to come out alone like this again, and I'll agree not to say anything about today to your grandmother." She smiled in conciliation.

The dark eyes moved over her as she sat with knees drawn up under her chin, her arms clasped loosely around her legs. An expression of shrewdness passed over his small, taut features. "You look different."

At first Kelly was so indignant she was tempted to turn him over her knee the way she had done to Judy just three years ago when she had been that age. Instead, she laughed with far more confidence than she felt.

"Of course I look different. Everybody looks different out on the beach when they forget who they are, forget their problems and just have a good time!"

An unexpectedly wistful light entered the somber dark eyes. "I wish I could be somebody else sometime."

Now Kelly's earlier motives were completely forgotten. He seemed so utterly alone and composed as he stood there. From the impeccable neatness of his clothing, she wondered if he knew how to enjoy himself like a normal child even when he escaped the watchful eyes of his protectors.

"Tell you what," she said in a conspiratorial voice, "why don't we both pretend to be somebody else? It'll be our own little secret. Let's see," she mused, rising from the sand. "I've always wondered what it would be like to be an acrobat. Watch this!"

She ran a few steps and turned a series of imperfect cartwheels. Then she turned and looked around for his approval, having forgotten every motive now except to bring a spark of spontaneity to this taciturn child. His face was expressionless except for a telltale quirk of the delicately shaped lips.

"Okay, buster," she demanded in mock belligerence. "*You* show me something better!"

After a long moment during which she could read something of the struggle going on inside him, he dropped to his knees and proceeded to demonstrate a headstand right there on the sand.

"Not bad," she admitted when he stood up, carefully brushing the sand from his head and then his knees. "It'd be a lot easier if you took off the shoes and socks and maybe the shirt, too," she suggested. Without hesitation he followed her directions, even removing the short pants. To her amazement he wore brief red swimming trunks underneath! What subterfuge for one so young!

His icy reserve quickly melted as they frolicked along the beach, each one striving to outdo the antics of the other. Finally Kelly became aware of the time and announced regretfully, "Sorry, Beach Partner, but I've got to get back to the house. You'd better come along, too, before someone discovers you're gone, if they haven't already."

He sobered instantly into the lonely, reserved little boy she had encountered earlier. "Hey, come on," she urged, "let's run in the edge of the water." Grabbing his small hand, she drew him along with her, and soon he was shrieking with laughter as they kicked and splashed their way back in the direction from which they had come.

"Come along." She resisted the insistent tugging of the small body. "I'll help you put your clothes on." He obeyed without protest, walking beside her up the slight incline. Suddenly the small hand gripped hers and she glanced down, surprised at the sudden transformation in his features and small body. Once again he was remote and aloof, like he was the first day she saw him enter Lady Jane's personal sitting room.

Following the trajectory of his vision, she stiffened in shock. Lounging against the trunk of a palm tree just yards away was Blair Mathison. Something about his watchful demeanor warned her he had been there for some time, taking in the abandon of his mother's secretary with his young son. Trembling with nervous reaction, Kelly was horribly conscious of the way the wet brown swimsuit was plastered to her body, the tangled disarray of her silvery blond hair free of the restraining barrette.

"Good afternoon, Mr. Mathison," she said stiffly, hurriedly shrugging into the protection of the short brown beach robe and fastening the barrette with hands so unsteady she had trouble manipulating the simple clasp. He didn't answer as she dropped to her knees and searched for her eyeglasses.

"Looking for these, Miss Lindsay?"

Fear leaped inside her at the insinuation in his voice, and she looked up to see him twirling the dark-rimmed spectacles in his lean brown fingers. "Yes, thank you. I'm virtually blind without them," she lied, and instantly suffered the repercussions.

"Is that so? I would have ventured to guess yours is a very weak prescription." The cutting irony of his voice was reflected in his merciless blue eyes.

Ignoring the comment, she began to help Jamie into his clothes, filled with a great foreboding that she had really blown everything this time. In spite of her deep concern for herself, she noted with a pang of sympathy how Jamie had retreated into his customary shell of reserve so unnatural for one so young. Realizing that he was probably as terrified inside as she herself was, she broke the awkward silence.

"Jamie was kind enough to accompany me along the beach this afternoon. We had a very pleasant time together, didn't we, Jamie?" There, she thought wretchedly. At least Jamie might survive intact even if she did not.

Without bothering to reply, Blair Mathison executed a mocking half-bow and ordered, "After you, Miss Lindsay."

There was no choice for her except to precede him along the path back to the house, Jamie clinging tightly to her hand. The trust implied in the grip of those small fingers aroused in her an anger at the people and the circumstances which denied this small child a normal, happy life. He was a poor little rich boy, if ever she had seen one.

The return walk seemed interminable, and she was relieved finally to see the bulk of the garage ahead. Lady Jane appeared on the terrace as they approached it and called out to the silent trio.

"Thank heaven you've found him!"

Kelly noticed with compunction how white her employer was, but the older woman's relief merged into indignation at the small boy. "Jamie, do you realize how worried everyone was about you? We thought—"

"It turns out Miss Lindsay took the boy for a walk on the beach," Blair Mathison interrupted, a deep note of skepticism bringing a tide of red to Kelly's salt-encrusted cheeks.

With a sinking in the pit of her stomach, she comprehended what Lady Jane had been about to say. How stupid of her not to realize that the first reaction to Jamie's absence would be fear of kidnapping. His father obviously did not want the sentiment spoken in front of him, but it was plain to her now why he hadn't been in the least pleased to find her enjoying a chummy afternoon with his son. He suspected her motives!

An unspoken message flashed between mother and son, and Lady Jane hustled her pensive young grandson inside, admonishing him all the while for frightening everyone, especially poor Eloise, by going off without telling anyone.

"Just a minute, Miss Lindsay."

The icy words halted Kelly in midstride. She turned around slowly, steeling herself for the worst.

"I want to know why you're taking the trouble to win the confidence of a seven-year-old child."

The ugly accusation in the softly spoken words touched off a wild anger inside Kelly. She drew herself up to her full height, her lips quivering with fury.

"Why don't you just come right out into the open and say what you're thinking, Mr. Mathison?" she blazed, all caution and sense of self-preservation forgotten. "I find it *revolting* that you assume no one could possibly have any interest in Jamie other than kidnapping him. If you'd really like to know my reasons for spending time with him this afternoon, I felt sorry for him. He's stuck here in this museum without any of the fun or"—she hesitated a moment as if suddenly aware of her own temerity, and her voice quieted—"or the love a normal child has. Jamie has everything money can buy, but he is a very lonely, unhappy little boy. Is there anything else you'd like to know, Mr. Mathison?"

The spurt of temper having subsided, she wanted nothing more now but to escape the keen blue eyes which swept her with a quizzical gaze. The brown robe no longer seemed sufficient protection, and she became conscious of her long bare legs already lightly tanned by the tropical sun.

"As a matter of fact, there are several things I'd like to know about you, Miss Lindsay," he drawled, "but they can wait until later."

By the time she reached the privacy of her own room, Kelly was trembling. She couldn't believe she had actually spoken the way she had to Blair Mathison. There was little chance now that she would be allowed to continue as Lady Jane's secretary, but she couldn't regret having defended herself the way she had. Every word was the truth. Try as hard as she could to adopt a servile role, her whole background had taught her to judge people on the basis of character and inherent qualities, not monetary worth. In a moment of anger she had reverted naturally to her own code of values.

The next morning Kelly crossed the lofty medieval hall and entered Lady Jane's sitting room, filled with foreboding. Lady Jane sat as usual at the ornate black lacquer secretary, where each morning she went through her mail and gave Kelly instructions concerning notes and letters to be written and telephone calls to be made.

She looked up now from a note she was reading and smiled absentmindedly. "Good morning, Kelly. Have a cup of coffee."

Kelly was astonished to hear her first name on Lady Jane's lips. Heretofore, she had been Miss Lindsay to her employer. To cover her confusion, she went over to the tray and poured herself some coffee from the heavy silver pot.

Lady Jane began talking as if nothing had changed since yesterday, as if Kelly had not stood out on the terrace and delivered a tirade to her aristocratic employer's son. There were the usual invitations to social functions, some to be accepted and others to be declined. In addition, Lady Jane announced her intention to give a big party herself, a garden dinner party with a Hawaiian motif.

Lady Jane showed more than her usual animation as she discussed the party preparations, making Kelly reflect that the older woman would be a happier person if she had more activities to occupy her time. Immediately she chided herself for being such a busybody. Two weeks at Casa de Fresa and already she was deciding what should be changed to make these fabulously rich people as happy as her family had always been! They would laugh if they knew her thoughts!

After Lady Jane had finished giving her instructions for the morning's work, Kelly automatically began to rise from her chair, intending to get started at once.

"There's no hurry to do that right now. Come over and have another cup of coffee."

Kelly was strangely wary at this change in daily routine. Just as Lady Jane had never before called her by her first name, neither had she encouraged her secretary to join her in anything remotely resembling a social situation. But greater surprises were in store.

"Kelly, are you happy here at Casa de Fresa?"

"Why, yes." Kelly struggled to keep her tone free of surprise. What on earth was going on here?

"That's good. I wanted to tell you I'm quite pleased with your work." She hesitated, looking uncomfortable, and Kelly groaned inwardly. Here it came—the sack. But Lady Jane's next words were not the dreaded dismissal. They were a quite astounding apology.

"You have an explanation due you for the way I've treated you. Miss Backen, your predecessor, was such a source of irritation to my son. She pursued him quite shamelessly. So I was quite determined to avoid such a situation again. That's one reason, and I'm sure you *wondered*, that I decided to have you take your meals with the servants. Ordinarily, of course, one of your education would not be placed in the same category as manual workers."

The blue eyes, which Kelly had often likened to shiny hard marbles, were gently conciliatory, if not actually beseeching. Kelly was speechless, her mind a blur as if several films were running concurrently on the same screen. Suddenly she understood the stiff-necked reticence of the butler and cook, who had realized, as she had not, that normal procedures were being violated. Another thought intruded itself with implications too disturbing to ignore. Lady Jane wasn't saying . . . she didn't mean . . .

"From now on, you will join the family for meals, my dear."

"Oh, but I don't mind at all eating with the servants," Kelly protested desperately.

Her employer didn't seem to be paying any attention. Her thoughts were back on the big party she was giving. "The invitations will have to be special . . . something clever . . ."

Kelly was oddly shaken over the exchange. She didn't *want* Lady Jane to be human and approachable, to call her "my dear" the way she had. Kelly much preferred her to remain the kind of character she wished to portray to the New Orleans television audience, autocratic and inflexible.

To her relief, Blair Mathison didn't seem to be around much during the day and was not present for lunch. Kelly assumed he was involved in the pursuits of the idle young rich. That evening he and Lady Jane had a dinner invitation, and the following evening she would be dining out with Philip Lawson. She welcomed this delay to sitting at the same table with the arrogant man who annoyed her more than any other man ever had. Somehow she knew he wouldn't be pleased his mother had included her secretary in the family meals.

As a result of that afternoon on the beach with Jamie, she had definitely made a friend. The young boy sought her company as soon as he arrived home from the exclusive private school he attended with other Palm Beach heirs and heiresses.

Though Kelly had decided to have nothing further to do with the boy after his father had all but accused her of kidnapping him, her resolution did not hold up under the appeal of solemn dark eyes. She marveled to think she had once considered him such an unnaturally quiet child. He talked a steady stream and asked her numerous questions about her own childhood, her family, her thoughts and reactions to countless "what if?" situations.

She discovered his longing to do so many things most children consider ordinary fare. He especially wanted to go to a movie in a regular movie theater. He had, of course, his own large color television set, and one of the Palm Beach families had a small private theater in their home. Jamie frequently went to movies which had been approved for children, the expense of renting the films shared by all the parents involved. But it wasn't the same thing, and he knew it.

"You've never been to the movies!" Kelly had exclaimed before she could bite back the words.

"Would you take me?" he asked wistfully, a glimmer of hope in the dark eyes.

"Why not?" She smiled, noting the transformation of

his small dark features and reflecting again how little he resembled his father. "Don't get your hopes up now," she warned. "Your grandmother may not like the idea."

"My dad, you mean," he said in a fierce tone.

The resentment in the dark eyes made her wish she hadn't even encouraged him to hope he would be allowed to go to the movies like an ordinary child. She kept forgetting he *wasn't* an ordinary child. He was the heir to a huge fortune and had to be protected from the horror of kidnapping.

She changed the subject and was relieved when he dropped the matter. Things were going smoothly and the last person she wanted to run afoul of was his father. Apparently Jamie had not dismissed the exciting possibility of attending a real movie, because the next afternoon he greeted her with the news that his grandmother had agreed to permit him to go with Kelly, as soon as a suitable film was playing. Jamie had already done his research and assured Kelly that a movie approved for a general audience was at that very time playing at the cinema located in one of the vast West Palm Beach shopping centers.

"Okay, you little scamp." She laughed, ruffling the fine dark hair. "I'll double-check with Lady Jane tomorrow, and if it's really okay with her, we'll go one night. How about hamburgers afterward?"

She might have offered him a very special and expensive gift the way his eyes widened with excitement. How strange that this child, who was waited on by servants and possessed every expensive toy one could imagine, became excited at the idea of eating at a hamburger chain restaurant! Life was terribly ironic.

Kelly herself was excited at the prospect of dining out with Philip. Most of all, she looked forward to slipping back into her old self and escaping the mesh of personalities at Casa de Fresa for a few hours.

The thought of wearing one of her nondescript outfits

bought especially for her secretary disguise was appalling. Instead, she wore a two-piece ensemble of indigo blue from her regular wardrobe. The tailored jacket made it demure and acceptable even for office wear, but the dress underneath was softly feminine with a scooped neckline and short cap sleeves. For the first time in what seemed like eons, she applied makeup to enhance her natural beauty rather than detract from it.

With a sensation of lightness and freedom, she surveyed herself in the mirror before drawing her hair back into the confinement of the barrette and slipping on the glasses which she had come to detest. She couldn't afford to take any chances of being seen without the rudiments of her disguise as she left the house. Once outside the estate grounds, she would remove both barrette and glasses.

At her request to go somewhere quiet, Philip chose a small Italian restaurant in West Palm Beach called Gino's. A totally unpretentious place, it had square tables covered with checkered oilcloth and chairs of plain painted wood. Philip assured her, however, that the food was outstanding. He insisted she try the spaghetti and clam sauce. Her wholehearted enjoyment of the food drew a wry comment from him.

"Don't tell me they're keeping you on bread and water in that place?"

"Quite the contrary," she objected. "I'm in great danger of becoming hopelessly obese."

"Do you dine with the great lady?" he asked curiously. Up until this time, the conversation had been general. Philip's initial inquiry about how things were going had met with a vague positive answer, and he had dropped the subject until now.

"Not at first," she replied, overcome by a strange hesitancy which surprised her. "Actually, Philip, she's not a bad person at all. Just old and, like many old people, a little at a loss as to how to make constructive use of her time."

"You're not getting soft, are you, kid? Feeling guilt pangs about what you're doing?" She colored becomingly under his piercing scrutiny. "Save your sympathy. Lady Jane Wessen is among the less than one percent of our population for whom no limitation exists except for their own lack of imagination. Don't be taken in by them, honey. They'll just use you the way they use everybody who isn't one of them. And don't think for one second you can ever be one of them, because you can't."

He took a sip of the dry red wine they were having with their dinner. "You've got to be tough and do the job you came here to do. It's a kind of test for you as a journalist, a hell of a proving ground, I admit, but you can do it."

Philip's words hit center target, arousing a great confusion inside Kelly. He had expressed the same attitude she had strongly espoused upon beginning her assignment, posing as a secretary in Lady Jane's household.

"Hey, whatever you do, don't look now," Philip warned in a low voice, "but the nobility is out slumming tonight."

At the startled question in Kelly's wide velvet brown eyes, Philip explained casually, "Blair Mathison just came in the door."

Kelly's heart set up an intolerable pounding at this news. Of all the incredibly rotten luck!

"This is horrible," she murmured to Philip, smiling as if she were making some comment about the delicacy of the wine or the pleasure of his company. "Is he looking at me?"

Undaunted, Philip smiled back at her, apparently enjoying the game. "He was. But now he's headed for the kitchen, it seems like. I think it's safe for you to look."

She didn't require more encouragement. There he was, tall and broad-shouldered, disappearing through

55

the door that presumably led back to the kitchen. Panic and dismay echoed in her voice. "Maybe I should leave before he comes back?"

"Sorry, honey, but he's definitely seen you. What's the point in skipping out? Do you think he'll recognize you the way you look now?" Philip's eyes moved appreciatively over the silvery sheen of her hair.

"Oh, I *hope* not," she moaned. "Why is it that every time I run into Blair Mathison, it's a disaster!"

Open curiosity shone in Philip's keen glance, but Kelly did not elaborate.

Finally he sighed. "Look, honey, relax. Obviously Mathison must have gone out the back way. He probably didn't want to be seen, either."

Philip made several more attempts to draw Kelly out of her introspective mood. She sensed in him an impatience for the way she resisted answering his probing questions about her experiences in the Casa de Fresa household. As far as he was concerned, he was simply expressing interest in a journalistic assignment and couldn't understand her reluctance to talk about her employer and family.

She would have explained her feelings to him if she had been able to understand them herself, but she didn't. Never had she intended to complicate matters with unwanted loyalties and sympathies. Everything had seemed so clear-cut when she had planned and carried out the imposture, which was so successful on the surface.

Eluding the questions became trying after a while, and she pleaded the need to get a full night's sleep. After the short drive back to the serenity of Casa de Fresa, she found herself once again inside the closed gates and sat for a moment engaged in a ridiculous battle with herself. How she had grown to detest the role she must continue to enact as long as she remained in Lady Jane's employ! Her fingers fumbled awkwardly with the barrette, and the heavy plastic glasses were as cumbersome to her heightened sensitivity as leg irons to a prisoner.

Sanford was waiting for her at the garage. His voice when he answered her ringing at the gate had been less succinct than usual, and she realized he had probably been awakened out of a sound sleep. He must have a set of the electronic gate controls in his apartment as well as in the main house.

He carried a large key ring and after a polite greeting opened a door at the rear of the house and stood aside for her to enter. She wished rather wistfully she could have stayed outside awhile in the luminous moonlight. How she would enjoy walking across the damp lawn down to the ocean. She needed solitude to explore the labyrinth of her own thoughts in the quiet and beauty of the immense solitude of sea and sky.

The evening left no aftermath of exhilaration, just a thoughtfulness tinged with faint worry as she wondered whether Blair Mathison had recognized her this evening. If so, what would be the consequences? She didn't have long to wait before she found out.

Feeling utterly alone in the huge quiet house, she climbed the steps of the tower, aware of the dankness, which made her feel she could really be in an ancient castle. Late at night like this, after having dinner in perfectly normal circumstances, it was difficult to believe her present situation was real. Was she really Kelly Lindsay, returning to her own room in this bizarre Moorish castle of a mansion?

Her room was dark, the only light that of the moonlight shedding a faint and ghostly illumination over the furniture. The effect fit her mood perfectly, and she didn't bother to press a light switch as she shrugged out of the jacket and kicked off a high-heeled sandal.

A slight movement in the room frightened her. Then

a quiet click and a lamp bloomed beside the sofa, revealing a lounging masculine form. Blair Mathison in her room! Kelly's heart thudded even harder against the prison of her rib cage as she stared incredulously at the man surveying her calmly with sardonic blue eyes.

"Turnabout's fair play," he mocked, reminding her of the time he had surprised her in his own bedroom.

"What do you want?" she managed to force past lips that trembled yet felt strangely stiff.

"That should be patently obvious, Miss Lindsay." He mimicked the prim tone she had used that day in the cottage. "I want to know who the hell you really are and why you're carrying on this masquerade."

The movement of his gaze made her suddenly conscious she had removed the jacket of her outfit and stood before him in the simple blue dress, the clinging bodice plainly revealing the shapeliness of her figure. One shoe was still on while one stockinged foot sank into the thick Oriental rug. Nervously she thrust her foot back into the sandal, fighting for time and trying to think fast.

Knowing there was little use in trying to bluff Blair Mathison, she decided on a blend of truth and deception she hoped would be convincing. "I really am Kelly Lindsay, and the reason for this 'masquerade,' as you put it, is that I wanted this job." She unfastened the barrette containing her pale silken hair and took off the glasses to reveal the full effect of her dark-lashed brown eyes. Standing before him, tall and slender and lovely, she balanced everything on the line now. If she didn't manage to convince him of her reasons for hiding her beauty, she would be gone tomorrow, if not tonight. And she didn't want to go yet.

"I'm tired, Mr. Mathison, of fending off male superiors. When I heard about this job as secretary to your mother, it seemed ideal as a change. Not too demanding and an opportunity to see how the other half lives."

It was difficult to tell if she was getting through. He certainly was looking her over thoroughly while she talked. "Luckily I got a hint ahead of time that she wanted someone plain, and . . ." She shrugged expressively and held up the dark-rimmed spectacles.

She held her breath as he slowly unfolded his length from the sofa and came over to stand in front of her. She had the choice of looking at the open throat of his shirt, a pale blue with narrow gray stripes, or tilting back her head to meet the impact of his quizzical blue eyes in a deeply tanned face. At close range like this she was alarmingly aware of his masculine virility.

"If Lady Jane's intentions were to hire someone plain"—his eyes narrowed to blue slits as they roved over her hair and face and then dropped to the rounded neckline of her dress—"she sure messed up with you, Kelly Lindsay." His gaze traveled down her figure as he continued in the same soft voice. "It's hard to hide those curves even in the atrocious clothes you usually wear around here."

Kelly wished desperately for the strength to move away from him, but her legs refused to cooperate. She stood there as if paralyzed while he lifted one lean brown hand and slowly, deliberately stroked the satin smooth blond hair falling to her shoulders. The hand slid down her back to her waist and without warning pressed her forward against him. Losing her balance, she had to grab at him to keep from falling.

She was helpless to stop him as he lowered his head and took her mouth in a kiss that demanded rather than asked for a total response. Partly as a result of shock, partly because she couldn't seem to resist the feelings he was arousing inside her, her lips parted under his and his tongue invaded the warm intimacy of her mouth.

She reeled drunkenly in a sensory world where time and prudence were temporarily suspended. The strong sure hands were caressing the slender curves of her body, cupping her breasts, and bringing to life the powerful responses to his masculine needs. Finally some shred of remaining judgment gave her the will to pull her face away from his and demur in a dazed tone, *"No."*

It wasn't a lucid, forceful plea, but under the circumstances it was the best she could do. Surprisingly, almost disappointingly, he released her and stood back, his chest rising and falling with his breathing, as if he had just run up a flight of stairs. Unless Kelly was suffering from an overactive imagination, he didn't look any more collected at the moment than she felt.

His eyes flicked over her pale bright hair mussed by his searching fingers, her dark brown eyes huge now with puzzlement, the soft lips still reddened from the pressure of his hard ones. A small smile lifted one corner of his firmly chiseled mouth. "We'd better postpone our discussion until tomorrow."

She caught his pointed look at the enormous canopied bed across the room and felt the blood heat her skin, and not just from embarrassment or indignation, either. Trying valiantly to clear her head of the confusion, she murmured, "But what about me?"

The quizzical smile on his lips broadened and his eyebrows lifted as he intentionally misunderstood her. She flushed a deeper color.

"I mean, are you going to let me stay? As Lady Jane's secretary, that is." Anxiety shone in the eyes as deep and dark as velvet pansies.

His eyes moved over her with a lingering attention that brought into quivering life every nerve and minute cell. "Why not?" he queried noncommittally. "Lady Jane seems to find your work acceptable, and Jamie would never forgive me if he misses that trip to the movies you promised him." The faint mockery in his tone stiffened her spine and brought her chin up a trifle.

His blue eyes searched her brown ones for a long, nerve-shaking moment, as if looking for something in the velvet depths. Then abruptly he was gone, leaving Kelly with the hopeless jumble of her emotions. When she took the job at Casa de Fresa, she hadn't bargained for Blair Mathison!

Chapter Five

The next two days were fraught with exasperation for Kelly. After Blair Mathison had left her room that night, she hadn't been able to sleep and arose the next morning still unsure of what to do next. After vacillating between continuing as if nothing had happened and making a clean breast of things with Lady Jane, she weakly decided on the former course, with modifications.

She dressed in a simple skirt and blouse from her real-life wardrobe, gathered her hair at the nape in a loose knot that was not so unflattering as the skinned-back style she had worn heretofore. The hated glasses were the only tangible vestige of her disguise.

"Why, Kelly, how attractive you look," exclaimed Lady Jane, sounding pleased, and Kelly knew she hadn't yet talked with her son that morning.

The usual routine did not vary that day or the next. The strain made Kelly want to scream. Any moment she expected to face the ordeal of being exposed as a phony by Blair Mathison. The prospect of facing him again set her nerves on edge with a bewildering amalgam of dread and anticipation. Then quite casually Lady Jane dropped the information that her son was out of town. Kelly was astounded by the surge of fury which set her teeth grinding against each other. Somehow she just *knew* Blair Mathison was laughing at her, fully aware of her anxiety. The man was a fiend, going off and leaving her to stew like this!

One development helped to take her mind off his diabolical behavior. Lady Jane received a letter from the Smithsonian Institution requesting information on her collection of Oriental rugs. At first she seemed not at all enthusiastic.

Almost idly Kelly questioned her about the collection and noted the older woman's evident knowledge of the wide variety of rugs she possessed. "Why don't you do it?" she pressed. "You certainly seem to know enough about the subject. And who knows? It might even turn into a book." Her voice warmed as she saw the possibilities of the project. Maybe this was just what Lady Jane needed to give her a sense of purpose.

"Well, perhaps I should." Lady Jane was uncertain now. "But I'd have to have pictures—"

"I could take those," Kelly insisted. "I'm really quite a competent photographer." She smothered the little guilt provoked by the thought of the excellent pictures she had already taken of Lady Jane's priceless rugs—without her permission.

"It *is* selfish of me to have these all to myself, I suppose." Underneath the indecision of her words, Lady Jane was already convinced. It showed in the sparkle of the blue eyes, the faint flush on the powdered cheeks.

They began that same day, and by late afternoon Kelly was wondering if she had unwittingly released a monster. Her mind was reeling with unfamiliar terms and names. In her ignorance she had thought of all Oriental rugs as "Persian," but learned it wasn't that simple. There were Caucasian rugs from the area called Caucasus, located between the Black Sea and the Caspian Sea. There were Turkish rugs, Turkoman rugs, rugs from Iran, India, East Turkestan and China. Within each of these geographical divisions were specific towns and nomadic tribes.

By the end of that first session with Lady Jane, Kelly was deeply impressed with her employer, who quite unexpectedly emerged as someone with considerably more than money invested in her collection. She possessed an astounding depth of knowledge about the history and techniques of rug making. She pointed out to Kelly a whole section of books on the subject in the library where Kelly worked every day at her desk. The older woman looked for a moment as if she might hug Kelly when she asked which of the books would be the best one for a beginner to read.

Lady Jane clearly assumed by this time that Kelly would eat dinner with her and Jamie in the impressive dining room. The vaulted ceiling and long table that would seat at least thirty was daunting to a girl from Houma, Louisiana. But fortunately Lady Jane dined at a smaller table set up in one corner.

Kelly was too disconcerted for speech the first evening when Lady Jane smiled at her secretary's furtive glance at the long, lace-covered expanse of the unused table under exquisite French chandeliers. "Ridiculously imposing, isn't it? That's the trouble with inheriting someone else's ideas of grandeur. If the house had belonged to my family rather than to my second husband's, perhaps it wouldn't seem so much like sacrilege to change things."

The succulent roast chicken became difficult for Kelly to chew. She was bursting with unasked questions, afraid she might discourage the mood of confidentiality. At the same time she was afraid that Lady Jane would reveal still more sensitivity to distort Kelly's sharply defined image of her as a rich imperious woman of little sensitivity. Some comment was required of Kelly, though, in the brief silence.

"You're thinking of your son and grandson, I suppose," she suggested tentatively. "Keeping things just the same for them."

Lady Jane made an inelegant sound, amazingly like a snort. "If it's up to Blair, he'll probably tear the place down as soon as I'm gone. According to him this house was inspired by a crazed, totally impractical mind. You've seen a sample of his taste in that cottage he renovated and decorated for himself."

Kelly secretly agreed with Blair Mathison. Her first thought when she viewed the mansion was incredulity that something so bizarrely out of place had been built in this tropical setting during the present century. She couldn't imagine anyone ever being really at home in this immense house.

"I talked to Blair long distance this afternoon," Lady Jane mentioned casually. "He has given permission for you to take Jamie to the movies. I've heard nothing else from that young man."

Kelly's heart had begun to race at the mention of a telephone call between her employer and her son. Surely Blair Mathison must have mentioned something about Kelly's being an impostor? What kind of game was he playing, anyway? Was he trying to cause her to have a nervous breakdown from the strain of waiting and wondering when the ax would fall?

"I should never have mentioned the possibility of a trip to the movies without first checking with you," Kelly apologized. "I'm afraid I didn't think of the possible dangers."

A shadow flitted across Lady Jane's bright-blue eyes.

"It's not easy on a child to be watched every minute. Maybe we've been overprotective since—" She stopped abruptly, as if suddenly aware of revealing something she hadn't intended to divulge.

Kelly wondered what had happened to cause such vigilance in the constant care of Jamie. Had there been some kidnapping attempt in the past? That question led quite naturally to others. In the weeks she had lived at Casa de Fresa, not one mention had ever been made about Jamie's mother, not even by Jamie. Blair Mathison's wife might never have existed, but Jamie was tangible evidence that she had. Who was she? What had happened to her? Those unanswered questions intrigued Kelly.

The newspaper revealed that a highly recommended movie for children was playing in West Palm Beach at one of the huge shopping centers. Jamie's ecstatic response to the news that she would honor her promise to take him to a real movie theater warmed Kelly's heart. She would have at least this one opportunity to show him the fun of a normal life.

Lady Jane made no objection to a rather tentative suggestion that they go a little early so that she and Jamie could walk around the shopping center. Afterward she planned to treat him to a hamburger in the noisiest, most garishly decorated fast-food restaurant she could find.

Kelly was looking forward to the outing with Jamie. She dressed in trim navy-blue slacks and a plaid cotton shirt. Taking even more liberties with her disguise, she folded a navy silk scarf lengthways and used it as a headband, leaving her silken blond hair to hang down to her shoulders. With gold hoop earrings she looked stunning until she settled the hated dark glasses on her nose, grimacing with disdain.

Jamie had come to her door twice to inquire if she was ready. Finally she laughingly suggested he wait for her in the car, which Sanford had already backed out of the garage. She had quietly but firmly refused Lady Jane's offer to have Sanford drive them in the limousine.

Her mouth curved into a smile of amusement as she emerged from the rear of the house, expecting to see Jamie seated impatiently in the passenger seat of her disreputable Volkswagen. She stiffened at the unexpected sight that greeted her. The Volkswagen was nowhere in sight. In its place was a sleek dark-green sports car with the top down. Jamie sat in the small back seat, and Blair Mathison stood leaning on the driver's door, his arms folded indolently across his chest and his mouth twisted in sardonic amusement at the open indignation on her face.

"Oh, no, not *you*," she blurted, and then colored when she realized what she had said. Resentment quickly settled in as she realized the truth: Blair Mathison didn't trust her enough to allow Jamie to go off in her company.

"How nice to be wanted," he countered ironically, and walked around to the open passenger's door, where he made a mocking little bow.

She stood immobile, momentarily paralyzed by the conflicting emotions besetting her. In his eyes was a bold reminder of the last time she had seen him. The man was probably used to his mother's secretaries falling into his arms the way she had. Now some basic instinct commanded her to refuse to get into that car with him.

"For Jamie's sake, let's not delay."

He had read her mind! His tone made it clear that if she didn't concede to this alteration in her plans, she wouldn't be allowed to take Jamie to the movie at all. She couldn't disappoint him, he was eyeing the two of them so hopefully. Besides, there was the matter of her real job in Palm Beach, gathering information for the feature. She couldn't really afford to antagonize her employer's son, not when she wanted to remain at Casa de Fresa until after Lady Jane's big party.

In the face of these pressures, she relented, walking stiffly around the car and getting into the low seat with as much dignity as possible. The maddening smile on Blair Mathison's face broadened, his white teeth bright next to the deeply tanned skin. Why, she wondered resentfully, did he have to look so suave and handsome, so exactly the way an idle rich playboy was supposed to look?

The powerful engine leaped into life at the turn of a key, and a faintly sarcastic remark popped out before she could swallow it. "Surely *you* didn't drive my car back into the garage?"

His blue eyes, alight with amusement, grazed her taut features as he comprehended instantly her insinuation that one such as he, having been born into a life of privilege, would be unable to cope with operating a lowly VW beetle.

He ignored the question and scolded mildly, "Now, now, Miss Lindsay. Your reverse snobbery is showing. Is it fair to hold against me what I couldn't help any more than Jamie can? Why don't you feel sorry for *me?*"

He was only making fun of her, and she knew it, but she couldn't resist a rejoinder. "You, unlike Jamie, are old enough to know that everyone in this world should make some contribution to society—even if you are born rich."

His low, spontaneous laughter awakened such intense frustration in her that she was tempted to jump out of the car and run back to the house. But it was already too late for her to act upon that irrational impulse, because he was turning the car out of the driveway onto Ocean Boulevard without making any inquiry as to destination. He obviously knew where the movie was showing and how to get there.

Kelly would have been less than human if she hadn't enjoyed the ride in the low-slung sports car. The seat was deeply cushioned and upholstered in a soft tan leather. The wind brushed her skin and lifted the hair from her shoulders. In the back seat, Jamie gave an excited bounce every now and then and talked excitedly, with none of the constraint he usually exhibited in the presence of adults.

Acutely aware that Blair glanced frequently at her, she finally allowed her eyes to meet his in a level stare that held a trace of belligerence. His firm mouth turned into an attractive smile. "Take the glasses off," he ordered, astonishing her so that she obeyed without question or comment. "There," he said smoothly, "no one seeing you at this moment would suspect you're a member of the hard-working middle class."

She compressed her lips into an uncompromising line and didn't speak.

"Seriously," he continued in a voice that indicated he was anything but serious, "don't you think it requires far more character to keep oneself entertained than to plod through life, out of necessity, toiling at a dull job?"

"I don't understand someone like you." Remembering Jamie in the back seat, she modified the sting in her voice. "You're obviously intelligent. You've had every benefit of education and travel. How can you not *do* something, accomplish something on your own? Oh, forget it!" she ended in exasperation, frustratingly aware of how widely separated they were by contrasting backgrounds and philosophy. There was no hope of communication between herself and Blair Mathison.

He seemed agreeable to dropping the subject. Soon he was parking the car at one side of the huge shopping center. If she had entertained even in passing the possibility that he might leave her and Jamie there with plans of picking them up later, she was disappointed. He strolled beside her toward the entrance of the mall, receiving numerous assessing glances from female shoppers.

Contrary to her expectations, he made no objection to their unhurried progress through the vast network of stores. Jamie was all shining brown eyes, exhilarated by the unfamiliar bustle of people of every conceivable age and physical description.

"You really think my son is missing out on some quintessential human experience because he doesn't mingle with the masses in shopping centers, Miss Lindsay?" The low chiding voice held an undertone of mockery. At the moment, he and Kelly were standing to one side observing Jamie as he mingled with a group of children watching a Ping-Pong competition out in the central commons of the mall.

"Yes, I do, Mr. Mathison," she replied crisply. "No child should be raised in a museum with no contact with reality. It's unnatural and limiting."

"And you think your contact with 'reality,' I believe you called it, has made you a better person than, say—myself?"

Something in the question itself, or perhaps in the penetrating blue eyes trained on her face, made Kelly uncomfortably aware of the duplicity of her position at Casa de Fresa. It was almost as if he *knew*. She brushed aside the disturbing thought immediately. Not a chance! The way Blair Mathison hated all journalists he wouldn't tolerate her presence another second if he knew the truth. Fortunately Jamie came up to them at that moment, and there was no need to answer the strange question.

Time for the movie drew near and the excited boy danced between Kelly and his father as they strolled in the direction of the cinema. Kelly's large brown eyes were luminous with tenderness as she listened to the boy's raptures about riding on the escalator. So intent was she upon the welcome transformation of this child, who had elicited her affection in such a short time, she wasn't even aware of the other people milling past them until a chance remark caught her attention.

"Aren't they a beautiful family! D'ya suppose her hair color is natural?"

Instinctively she glanced over at Blair and knew from the amused glint in his eyes that he too had heard the comment. A becoming blush surged beneath the golden tan of her cheeks.

"Well, is it? Natural, I mean?" His eyes flicked meaningfully to the pale shimmer of her hair and then returned to her face, observing with interest the battle ensuing there between embarrassment and amusement. Her sense of humor won, as it usually did, tilting the corners of her mouth. She glanced at him with her dark eyes alight with mischief.

"Every woman has her little secrets, doesn't she?"

His low, rich laughter followed the merest pause, spreading a delicious warmth through her. At that moment they arrived at the entrance of the cinema, and Jamie claimed her attention, pulling her over in front of a large full-color advertisement of the movie they were to see. Kelly didn't have time to reflect upon the brief speculative expression which had flashed in Blair's eyes before he had laughed appreciatively at her quip.

It was only minutes later, seated in the dim interior of the theater beside Jamie, that she mulled over her own words and recalled his lightning reaction, his censure quickly covered by laughter. Once again she had that uneasy thought that perhaps he wasn't fooled by her explanation of her disguise. But surely he wouldn't allow her to remain in his mother's house another minute if he suspected the truth? Not the way he felt about journalists and the invasion of his privacy!

No, silly, you're imagining things, she mocked herself, stifling the uneasiness and accepting instead a more obvious explanation of the briefly revealed criticism she had detected in Blair Mathison. No doubt his deep-seated arrogance was offended at even the most playful suggestion that he might be married to a low-ranking commoner like herself.

Pride stiffened her posture when he returned from the concession area in the lobby, hands laden with large cups of buttered popcorn. Her first instinct was to withdraw into a cool shell of indifference, to show him unmistakably that she entertained no desire to ingratiate herself with him as her predecessor had reportedly attempted to do. Again she had to remind herself that this outing was for Jamie's benefit, not hers, and she would not spoil it. She hadn't invited his millionaire playboy father to accompany them, and whatever his reasons for doing so, she refused to allow his presence to disconcert her.

She crunched a mouthful of popcorn loudly, ignoring the fact that their seating arrangement had been altered upon Blair's return from the concession stand. When they had first entered the theater and claimed seats, Jamie had been in the middle seat. Now Kelly found herself between him and his father. Blair must have accidentally taken a different aisle and found himself entering the row of seats on her side, and she had no intention of acknowledging the change.

It was impossible, though, not to be aware of the man beside her. His long muscular body filled the space designed for a person of average height, and he shifted sideways to accommodate his long legs, causing his knee to press intimately against hers. The contact caused a ridiculous tingling sensation which spread alarmingly throughout her entire body. Feeling the vibrations of his amusement, she turned her head toward him, pulled by a powerful compulsion beyond her control. Something jolted inside her as her eyes met his. Her lips curved irrepressibly in response to the white gleam of his smile. His charm was quite overwhelming at such close quarters when he looked at her like that, shattering all her firm resolutions to regard him with the utmost calm.

"Hope you're ready for a heartrending plot," she murmured, trying with desperation to break the flow of something disruptive between them. The previews for upcoming shows had begun and the flickering light from the screen played across his strong, masculine features.

"Under certain circumstances, I can stomach anything," he countered with a teasing note that cut off her breath.

Fortunately Jamie said something, awakening Kelly to the dismaying realization of how absurdly she was behaving. Taking her unsettled emotions firmly in hand, she deliberately turned away toward the boy, bending solicitously to check upon his comfort. Hoping her movements did not appear too obvious to the man beside her, she shifted her position so that her leg no longer touched his and resolutely trained her attention upon the screen.

The basic plot of the movie was a familiar one concerning the separation of a boy from his beloved dog and the long chain of hair-raising circumstances both undergo before they are finally reunited. The appealing mongrel bore a startling resemblance to a pet from Kelly's own early childhood years, and before long she was as immersed in the movie as Jamie, who sat spellbound.

One particularly emotional scene brought tears to Kelly's eyes, blinding her so that the screen became a colorful blur. Blinking hard, she glanced surreptitiously at Blair, hoping he hadn't noticed how sentimental she was. He appeared to be concentrating upon the screen himself, but a hand came over to capture one of hers, lean strong fingers interlocking with her own slender soft ones.

It was fortunate for her that the movie was almost over at this point, because her attention was sorely disrupted by the warm, firm contact of his flesh. He was causing havoc with the normal tempo of her heartbeat in spite of a severe lecture she delivered to herself about adolescent emotions.

With immense relief she heard the background music swell into a finale and saw the words "The End" flash across the screen. Very casually she extricated her hand from his warm clasp and turned inquiringly to Jamie, his enrapt expression quelling the selfish urge to cover her own confusion with meaningless chatter. She understood instinctively how emotionally spent the young boy felt after having lived imaginatively through every tense moment of the movie.

"Ready to go, dear?" she asked gently, unable to resist smoothing her hand across his dark fine hair.

He looked up at her with eyes too large for his small sensitive features and nodded absentmindedly, as if just now becoming aware of his companions. Then with the resilience of childhood, he emerged from the trancelike state and talked excitedly about the movie.

Kelly held the small hand tightly as they walked to the end of the row and entered the crowded aisle. Without warning, two strong hands clasped protectively at either side of her waist, tightening when several times she was jostled against him. She could feel the strength of his chest against her back and could smell the musky male scent of him, a heady blend of warm flesh and spicy soap. She fought the compelling urge to lean against him, to succumb to her senses.

Once out in the lobby, the crowd dispersed quickly, allowing for freer movement. Jamie, however, appeared to enjoy holding Kelly's hand and made no attempt to pull away, nor did his father take one hand from her waist as the three of them walked the short distance across the pavement to the car. She couldn't possibly be unaware of the glances they received from passersby and flushed with the memory of that remark overheard earlier, "What a beautiful family!"

The absurdity of that misconception struck her with renewed force at the sight of the dark-green sports car. It symbolized clearly the tremendous barrier between Blair Mathison and herself, people from two totally different worlds. She *must* remember at all times to fight the insidious attraction this man held for her. She *must* keep at the forefront of her mind that he was an idle playboy who would toy with her as the mood struck him and then drop her like a used plaything when he became bored. Yet in spite of her awareness of the danger, there was no denying his power over her senses. She must be very careful to keep Blair Mathison at a safe physical distance or she would be in great trouble.

"Where to now?"

A humorous undertone in the light query mocked the somberness of her thoughts. The object of her reflections was regarding her with quizzical blue eyes, eyebrows quirked comically. An irrepressible giggle bubbled up in her throat at the mental image flashing through her mind.

"I promised Jamie we'd have a hamburger after the movie. Right, Jamie?" She glanced over her shoulder, encouraging the expectant youngster's support, and wasn't disappointed at his enthusiastic reaction.

Their arrival at a large, brightly lit hamburger chain restaurant created quite a stir, the low-slung expensive car roaring to a stop between two modest economy compact cars. Kelly bit back the impulse to accuse him of being a show-off in front of a bunch of impressive teenage boys and their dates, but her thoughts must have shown plainly in her expression. Blair shrugged, a rueful smile twisting his mouth, and amazed her with the unexpectedness of his wry comment.

"If you've got it, flaunt it!"

He laughed delightedly at the incredulity on her face

and came around quickly to open her door, still chuck-ling.

Jamie's excitement was evident for all to see as the three of them trooped inside to take their place at the end of the line of people awaiting a turn at the counter. It was one of those assembly-line kinds of places where you order and move down a few feet to pick up the food a minute later. Kelly halfway expected Blair to insist that she and Jamie go and sit at a table while he remained in line and got their food, but he made no such suggestion.

She watched with curiosity as father and son studied the signs stating the limited fare of the restaurant and discussed Jamie's possible choices. This was the first evidence of warmth Blair Mathison had shown toward his son in her presence, and she found the brief scene strangely touching. Fleetingly she wondered again what had happened to cause Blair's customary detachment from his son. Did it have something to do with whatever had caused the divorce between him and his wife? It seemed a question she wasn't likely to have answered by the time she would have to leave Casa de Fresa.

When their turn came to step up to the counter and place their order, Jamie hung back shyly at first and then at a nod of encouragement from his father, announced: "Hamburger, french fries and a chocolate shake." From the proud tilt of his small head, he might just have accomplished some extraordinary feat, Kelly noted to herself with tender amusement.

"And what about you, sweetheart?" Blair pushed her forward, his hands gripping her shoulders posses-sively. She nearly choked at his blatant mimicry of the typical man of the house out for a meal with the wife and son.

"I'll just have a cheeseburger and a Coke, honey," she purred, casting him what she intended to be an adoring-wife smile.

"Get whatever you want," he insisted in loud magnanimous tones and delivered his own choices, extracting his wallet from a hip pocket.

Kelly's shoulders shook with suppressed laughter as he carried their laden tray to a vacant table. The chairs, constructed of molded orange plastic, were bolted to the floor. The garish interior of the dining area was brightly lit, and a jukebox blared rock music from the rear.

Eyes brimming with laughter, she couldn't help commenting for the benefit of all those nearby, "You always take us to nice places."

"Yeah, this place is *neat!*" Jamie exclaimed, missing entirely the double meaning of her remark. He attacked his food with an appetite, and Kelly didn't have the heart under the circumstances to remind him of his manners.

Her own food tasted delicious in spite of the noisy atmosphere. The conversation, what there was of it, centered mainly around the movie and was dominated by Jamie's opinions. Overall, he declared it as ranking high among the best movies he had ever seen and expressed the hope that the three of them might make a habit of this type of excursion. He didn't press the point, as a normal child might have, when Kelly made a noncommittal reply and his father merely looked thoughtful.

The drive back to the estate was quiet, each of them absorbed in private thoughts. Earlier that same day Kelly would have scoffed bitterly at the notion of herself being relaxed in Blair Mathison's company.

When they arrived at the formidable gates of the estate, he reached into the glove compartment and pressed a small remote-control gadget that opened the gates before them, as if by magic. The night air was redolent of flowering shrubs and the faint salty tang of the nearby ocean. A deep serenity lay over the dark grounds, and all too soon the car slowed to a stop beside the vast bulk of the mansion. Kelly wished she could stay outside for a while, delay going back inside those massive walls where she would have to resume once again the role she found more and more difficult to sustain.

The original outward disguise had already changed considerably until there was little left of it, except the hated eyeglasses. The smug, precise manner, too, had all but disappeared now that she had become deeply engrossed with Lady Jane's work on the report for the Smithsonian and the preparations for the big gala party. Ironically the closer she came to being herself, the more onerous was the burden of her imposture.

"Wait here."

The low command stopped her as she swung the door open and began to step from the car. She might have protested and even disobeyed the order had it not coincided so perfectly with her own deep instincts.

As soon as he had disappeared through the rear entrance, a drowsy Jamie in his arms, she was gripped with apprehension and disgust at her traitorous submissiveness. What did Blair Mathison want of her. What did he expect to gain? And why hadn't her better judgment alerted her to avoid being alone with him?

So involved was she with these mental churnings, it seemed to be only seconds before he was back, tall and undeniably masculine as he stood beside the still-open passenger's door. She sat, immobilized in uncertainty, one leg in the car and one foot on the driveway pavement.

"It's much too early for sleep," he said. "I hoped you would keep me company for a while." The deep, quiet resonance of his voice flowed over her overwrought nerves, a calming balm restoring her common sense.

"It is a beautiful night." Somehow her soft response didn't seem irrelevant.

His next actions took her by surprise. He bent and gently replaced her foot inside the car, closed the door, and came swiftly around to slide under the wheel. Kelly asked in puzzlement, "Where are we going?" But even before the words were out, she already knew.

"Unless you have some objection, we'll have a drink at my place." He shoved the stick shift into gear but did not release the clutch, waiting for her affirmation.

"Well, if you promise not to take advantage of your position as Lord of the Manor," she quipped, and felt his gaze on her features for a long moment before he let in the clutch and eased the car smoothly into motion.

She was secretly pleased with her comment. It set things clearly into perspective. She was a "mere secretary" in his mother's employ, while he was the pampered and spoiled heir to a vast fortune and would never have to work a day in his life. Most of all, she wanted it absolutely plain that *she* understood their respective positions and wanted nothing from him.

"I *do* envy you this," she admitted a few minutes later, seated next to him on the front steps of the cottage. Before them stretched the mighty ocean, mysterious and seductive under a huge canopy of sky studded with stars. The husky rhythmic pulsing of the tide as it encroached upon the sandy beach and then receded, only to surge forward again, seemed to put a spell over Kelly. She wasn't a fatalist, but somehow she was aware of how inexorable are the workings of nature, the passing of time. The aspirations and strivings of human beings like herself seemed rather insignificant, even petty, at the moment.

The man beside her took a sip from the glass in his hand and didn't respond to her comment for several moments. He appeared engrossed in his own thoughts, perhaps in his own response to the nocturnal beauty spread out before them.

"This place *is* special," he said reflectively. "I'd hate to have to give it up."

"But why on earth would you?" she exclaimed.

79

Suddenly she remembered a comment Lady Jane had made about her son's attitude toward the estate. Kelly was curious to hear from him what he would do with the ancestral mansion when it passed into his hands.

"You wouldn't consider selling Casa de Fresa after Lady Jane—er, I mean—" Her voice fumbled for a word less harsh than the obvious one.

He expelled a sigh and answered in a voice almost angry. "What else *can* I do? You have no conception of what it costs to maintain that museum, as you so aptly described it, not to mention ten acres of grounds. That's the other side of the coin that the majority of people never even consider," he continued bitterly, "the burden of inheritance."

"I see what you mean," Kelly said slowly, and for the first time she really did comprehend some of the drawbacks of being in Blair Mathison's shoes. "It's a question of family tradition and sentiment versus practicality. If the decoration of this cottage is an indication of your tastes—and according to Lady Jane you decorated it yourself—you probably will not desire to live in the main house, even if you remarry and have other children—"

"That's definitely out of the question."

His curt interruption brought a flood of warmth to her cheeks. She hadn't meant to probe, but her words could be construed as prying into his marital plans for the future. The silence was a little awkward, and she determined to change the subject to a safer one.

"Have you lived here long—in the cottage, I mean?" She idly raised the stemmed glass in her hand and pressed its cool, moist bell against her cheek before taking a sip of the white wine. This evening all her senses seemed oddly heightened.

"You think it's strange that I don't live in the main house with my mother and son."

The abruptness of his statement combined with the

harshness of his tone made Kelly stare at him in surprise. "I'm sorry . . . I didn't mean to pry," she began apologetically, and then shrugged. "Your relationship with Jamie *isn't* exactly the normal parent-child one," she said, picking her words carefully. In the back of her mind glimmered the hope that perhaps she could press Jamie's suit with his seemingly indifferent father. "And he is a delightful child—intelligent, likable, attractive. Of course, he's small-boned and doesn't resemble you . . ." Her voice trailed off uncertainly as she became aware of the tenseness of the man beside her. Anger almost like a tangible force reached across the distance between them, scorching her protesting soul.

"Oh, no. He *must* be your son," she gasped. "How can you think—I mean, how *can* you! The poor kid!" She stopped, at a dead loss for words. No wonder Blair was so detached with Jamie. He didn't believe Jamie was really his own son!

"God knows why I should tell *you*—" The terrible anger in the man next to her on the steps seemed to dissipate, leaving behind only calm weariness. She wondered briefly at the import of his words before he continued. What could he possibly fear from confiding in her? Unless—

"Denise, my former wife, wasn't 'one of us,' as the saying goes. I married her for spite over the violent objections of my mother, against the advice of all my friends." He raked one hand restlessly through his hair and sighed. "At age twenty-four I was so sure I knew more than anyone else. My mother had just remarried, and I was furious at what I thought was a betrayal of my father's memory. I couldn't fathom what she saw in George except a meaningless title. He didn't have any money to speak of.

"In all honesty, though, I can't blame anybody but myself for the mess I got myself into. I became a beach

bum—beard, ragged clothes, bare feet, the whole bit.
Denise was a singer in a club in Cocoa Beach. She fit
perfectly into my scheme of rebellion."

He drained the contents of his glass and tossed the
remaining ice cubes out on the lawn. "I suppose you're
wondering how someone could go so far as marriage
just to spite his family." At her nod, he sprawled back
on his elbows, his long legs spread in front of him on
the steps. "You're also wondering, no doubt, why my
mother didn't pull me in line with the traditional threats
of disinheritance. The answer to the first question is
that I fell for the biggest female hoax in the world. The
second answer is that my father's will made it impossible for me to be cut off."

Kelly cleared her throat. "What *is* the 'biggest female
hoax in the world'?"

His laugh came harshly, grating her nerves. She
reflected irrelevantly that she wouldn't like to have this
man as an adversary. Underneath his sophisticated
exterior ran a vein of cruelty.

"I refer to it as the Pregnancy Pretense, capital P's."
At her sharply indrawn breath, he laughed again, the
sound no less abrasive to her ears. "Oh, she wasn't
pregnant with Jamie. That came later. As soon as we
were married, she unfortunately 'lost' the baby she
never had carried in the first place. The truth was soon
out of the bag, and I discovered I had been *had* in more
ways than one."

His voice altered unexpectedly so that it held a note
of pity. "Poor Denise. It turned out I didn't know her
at all. She wanted everything I was trying to turn my
back on—the life of the Beautiful People. When I
point-blank refused to go along with her, she tried to go
it alone. She maneuvered herself into Casa de Fresa
with Lady Jane and George and joined the swinging
young crowd who jetted from the Riviera to Newport
and back to Palm Beach."

"Where were you all this time?" Kelly was caught up in an inexplicable sense of dread.

"Here and there. Europe, Asia, South America. At the time it didn't much seem to matter. Then finally I decided to come back here and face up to things. Whereupon I immediately discovered I was to be a father." She could feel the mockery of his gaze raking her tense form as she sat hunched forward, arms hugging her knees. "Now perhaps you understand a little better my constraint with Jamie?"

"But that isn't fair," she protested hotly. "None of this was Jamie's fault. How can you hold it against him? Under the circumstances, I don't understand why—"

"His mother didn't want him," he interrupted curtly.

"Why didn't she have an abortion?"

He shrugged. "She had some simplistic notion his real father would marry her. Shows how little she understood that crowd. Instead she had to settle for a considerable sum of money and the galling realization that she was no longer welcome in a single Palm Beach home once she was divorced from me."

Kelly flinched at the hardness in his voice. Didn't he have any feelings? "Has she shown any interest in Jamie since that time?"

"In a manner of speaking." His voice was heavy with sarcasm. "She ran through the money in a couple of years and demanded more, threatening to sue for custody of Jamie. I invited her to go right ahead. If the courts ruled in her favor, she was welcome to him. Naturally she didn't really want him. Her next move was a little more desperate."

"My God, no," Kelly begged, somehow knowing what he would reveal next.

"My God, yes," he mocked. "Jamie's own mother, with the collaboration of her boyfriend of the moment, kidnapped him. And we paid, of course. Now maybe you can appreciate our excessive caution."

Kelly was utterly appalled at the story she was hearing. The whisper of the ocean seemed as solemn as a dirge. The brightness of the misshapen moon was smothered in a blanket of clouds.

"Not a pretty story, is it, Kelly Lindsay?" the man beside her asked softly, straightening from his sprawling position and slipping an arm around her waist. She didn't demur when he curved his other hand along the contour of her cheek and turned her troubled face toward him. "One must be very careful about becoming entangled in the lives of other human beings." As he spoke these cryptic words, he slowly lowered his head toward her until his warm breath fanned her face. She held her breath, awaiting the inevitable.

His lips caressed hers slowly and then slid across her cheek and down to an earlobe before descending tantalizingly to her neck, his free hand pushing aside the collar of her shirt. The heat of his breath on her sensitive skin ignited a small flame that spread rapidly throughout her body, producing a languor oddly at variance with the heightened drumbeat of her heart.

"Hold me," he commanded in a husky voice, bringing his lips back to her mouth and claiming it with increasing urgency. Her arms slid obediently around his waist, her hands reveling in the smooth firmness of the muscles in his taut back. Her touch inflamed his passion, and he kissed her hungrily, his mouth forcing hers open, his tongue exploring and arousing a wild response that made her hands insatiable for the feel of him.

Never before had she permitted a man the liberties he took without asking. His hands molded her waist and hips, cupped her breasts, thrust impatiently inside her blouse to feel the soft fullness and the hardened nipples. With a groan he pulled her over on his lap, crushing her against him so that she could feel his ragged breathing, the erratic thumping of his heart against her breasts. Before she could guess his intent, one hand stroked her thigh expertly, awakening in her an aching need that overwhelmed principles to which she had clung through four years of college.

"Do you want me to make love to you?" His low voice vibrated with passion.

"Yes, oh, yes," Kelly heard herself murmur. At that moment she wanted nothing more in the world than to have this man possess her, satisfy the consuming fever in her loins, know her intimately as no man before him had. Afterward she would be irreparably changed, emotionally as well as physically, but she couldn't help herself. The need was too great to consider the consequences, and she knew intuitively that the experience would be something wonderful and special to her, even if it had no significance for him.

"You've never been to bed with a man before, have you, Kelly?" Some timbre in his voice alerted her. The precious moment was slipping away. What had gone wrong?

"No," she admitted unsteadily.

"You realize I have no intention of marrying you."

"I never expected you to," she replied quietly, and pressed her lips against the corded muscles of his neck, wishing he would stop talking. Without warning he shoved her roughly off his lap, stood up and stared out at the dark ocean.

"Wh-what's wrong?" she asked in hurt puzzlement.

"Just be grateful I'm a damned fool and don't ask any more questions." he said harshly.

Kelly was thankful for the darkness. It took all her self-control to suppress the tears of humiliation which threatened any second to overcome her rigid composure. She walked numbly beside him as he escorted her in total silence through the hushed grounds, the powerful flashlight in his hand illuminating the way past towering palm trees and flowering oleanders and hibiscus.

The huge shadowed bulk of Casa de Fresa seemed to

her overwrought imagination like an ancient prison as he unlocked a rear door and stepped aside for her to enter. Pride rose to her defense. She would die before she allowed him to perceive how truly devastated she was at this moment. Squaring her shoulders, she managed a note of light irony.

"Thanks for a most interesting evening." Before he could reply, she fled through the open door.

Chapter Six

Seldom in her life had Kelly wept with such wild abandon and never before with the bitterness and utter hopelessness that produced a seemingly endless reservoir of tears. More than anything else in the world, she longed for the blessed oblivion of sleep, which was denied to her for long hours as her memory cruelly replayed the humiliating scene on the steps of Blair Mathison's cottage.

How she wished now she had stood her ground at the price of disappointing Jamie, if matters had come to that. Her first encounter with Blair Mathison, when he discovered her exploring his cottage, had aroused all her self-protective instincts. Somehow she had known she could be vulnerable in his hands. Just how vulnerable hadn't been revealed until tonight, when she had shamelessly offered herself to him, and he had refused.

The next morning she was relieved to learn from Lady Jane that Blair had already departed on one of his unexplainèd trips. Kelly wondered if he had left in order to avoid his mother's secretary.

"It would be so much more convenient for him to make his permanent headquarters in New York, but he indulges my preference to live here." Lady Jane's voice was tinged with regret.

The comment puzzled Kelly greatly, but she refrained from asking any questions that would inevitably lead to a discussion of Blair. Her carefully controlled emotions couldn't stand the strain after the events of last night. Still she couldn't suppress her curiosity. Why would Blair need to live in New York? Surely the city offered much in entertainment and theatrical glamour, but so did many other places in the world frequented by the jet set. If he were engaged in business, though he had given no indication that he was, she would have understood Lady Jane's reasoning.

As best she could, Kelly dismissed all consideration of the man who had rejected her so contemptuously. She reminded herself of the real purpose of her presence at Casa de Fresa and made a mental checklist of pictures she still wanted to take. The opportunity was unlimited now that she had volunteered her photographer's skills for Lady Jane's Smithsonian report. Her camera had become a familiar and accepted part of her person.

In any case, she was much too busy to mope. Occasionally she wondered somewhat ruefully if she hadn't created a monster when she convinced her employer to make an informative inventory of her priceless rug collection for the Smithsonian Institution. The woman who had previously made revealing statements about the idleness of her life had become a dynamo of purposeful energy, driving both herself and Kelly from early morning until late afternoon.

Kelly found the whole project fascinating. On the third day following the disastrous trip to the movies with Jamie, she and Lady Jane worked all day in the vast stone hall, so like the main chamber in a medieval castle. Late in the afternoon Kelly was thoroughly engrossed in photographing an extremely rare *kilim* rug, woven in the seventeenth century in Kāshān, Persia, using the split-tapestry technique. Lady Jane busily jotted down notes while Kelly focused the camera, wishing privately for better lighting.

"Notice the central medallion. That's a very old Chinese motif depicting the combat between the dragon and the phoenix. Actually the design was probably copied directly from Chinese porcelain," Lady Jane explained.

"I'll get a close-up detail of the medallion," Kelly replied absently.

"You need more light." The deep masculine voice uncannily echoed Kelly's own frustrated train of thought, and she jumped visibly at the totally unexpected interruption. How on earth had Blair Mathison crept up so close behind her without making a sound? Her heart pounded at his nearness, and she gripped the camera to conceal the trembling of her fingers.

"You're right, of course. I do need better lighting in here," she said evenly, forcing her eyes to meet his. How handsome and manly he was, attired in crisp white slacks and a navy knit pullover that hugged his broad shoulders. He could have posed for a glossy advertisement featuring a rich playboy, she reflected bitterly, conscious of a painful twisting in her chest.

"I see your eyesight has improved." His ironic gaze missed nothing as it swept over fine-spun silvery hair no longer imprisoned in the barrette but shoved carelessly behind her ears and settled on her dark, soft eyes. His eyes didn't stop at her face, though. They raked the length of her slender form, lingering on the swell of her breasts under the plain shirt, the curve of her trim hips under the denim skirt.

Kelly held her breath in nameless terror, expecting at any moment some kind of verbal onslaught. His insolent survey held a contempt that drained the strength from her limbs and lent a sallow cast to the golden tan of her cheeks.

Lady Jane, oblivious to the tense atmosphere or preferring to ignore it, broke the spell. "Kelly finally admitted she doesn't need those hideous spectacles unless she's reading fine print. The silly girl wears them to appear more efficient," she announced breezily. "Besides, they only get in the way when she's photographing, as you can imagine. Now, what shall we do about this lighting situation?" she demanded of her son, her blue eyes clearly impatient with this interruption in her work.

The taunting expression on his face changed as he transferred his gaze to his mother, every inch the imperious aristocrat waiting for her wishes to be executed. "You're really into this project, aren't you, *ma mère?*" he observed curiously.

"I certainly am," she replied crisply. "If this goes over well, I intend to write a book. At the moment there isn't a comprehensive one on the subject."

This was news to Kelly, who struggled to control the astonishment flashing across her features. She relaxed a bit, grateful to no longer be the subject of discussion. Her relief, though, was short-lived.

"I see. And is Miss Lindsay going to stick around and aid you in this ambitious undertaking?" A faint note of scorn tinged his voice, stiffening Kelly's spine and tightening her lips. She was on the verge of a retort that might result in her dismissal from Casa de Fresa that very evening when her employer came to her defense with a sharpness that left both Kelly and Blair Mathison momentarily speechless.

"If I have anything to do with it, she will. And I won't have you badgering her either just because she has a mind of her own and doesn't chase after you the way some of my previous secretaries have done." Lady

Jane paused in the midst of her lecture and bestowed a look of affection upon Kelly. "I'd like to meet your parents someday, my dear, and tell them what an admirable job they've done in rearing their daughter. Now, about the lighting problem."

Kelly's eyes involuntarily clashed with Blair's, the latter brilliant with incredulity and something else oddly akin to amusement. She dropped her gaze after a breathless moment, unable to respond lightly to Lady Jane's unexpected and staunch defense.

Blair addressed a brisk question to her concerning the proper illumination she required for clear photographs of the rugs. Taking his cue, she answered in a businesslike manner and then added, "Of course, we *could* solve the problem by taking them one by one to a room with greater natural lighting, but that would necessitate a lot of extra effort."

He dismissed that idea with a peremptory wave of one tanned shapely hand. "That won't be necessary now that you've explained what is needed. What kind of film are you using?"

Automatically she replied to that and several more questions, not stopping to wonder why he was asking them. It was some time later that she realized he had quite skillfully ascertained that her technical knowledge of photography went far beyond that of the casual camera buff.

Lady Jane soon grew restive at the conversation and cut in, "We've done enough for one day anyway. Kelly, I'm sure by now Jamie is waiting impatiently for you at the pool." She turned to her son. "I didn't expect you back so soon. Did you have any success with—"

Kelly didn't wait to hear the rest of the question or the answer. Seeing her opportunity, she fled to her room and changed into a swimsuit, the dark brown one she had worn the day she had encountered Jamie alone on the beach.

It was plain she had won the child's trust that day, and since then he sought her company as often as possible. Lately they had fallen into the routine of spending a half-hour or more swimming and frolicking in the pool prior to changing for dinner. Kelly loved to swim and found the vigorous exercise just what she needed to help her relax. Jamie's company was genuinely enjoyable for her, too. It was amazing how close the two of them had grown, so much so that it would wrench her heart to leave him as she must do soon. She only wished she could be assured that his life would be filled with a little more love and companionship in the future.

Fifteen minutes later she stood on the diving board, her wet nylon suit clinging to the supple lines of her figure, demonstrating to Jamie the technique for executing a simple dive. She performed one effortlessly, surfaced and swam over to the side of the pool where he watched, dark eyes agleam with enthusiasm.

"Can I try it now, Kelly?" he begged.

"Honey, we'd better get your grandmother's permission first," she refused gently.

"Why don't you get his father's permission?"

She swung her gaze in the direction of the masculine voice with its familiar note of mockery. Blair stood behind the diving board, wearing brief white swimming trunks that molded his hips and contrasted vividly with his sun-bronzed skin. Kelly stared, uncomfortably aware of his masculine virility in the skimpy attire. He must have approached from the direction of the terrace without her being aware of his presence. Had he observed her diving demonstration?

She shrugged offhandedly. "Well, *does* Jamie have his father's approval?"

"He does. Right after I give him another demonstration."

He climbed the ladder with the lithe muscularity of a

fit athlete and balanced on the end of the springboard, a superb specimen of masculinity. His dive was perfect.

Show-off! was Kelly's private reaction, and she had the uncomfortable intuition as he approached her with a few powerful side strokes that he read her thoughts. His white teeth gleamed against the deep tan of his face. His blue eyes between thick wet lashes were brilliant with a quizzical light. The nearness of those broad tanned shoulders interfered with her normal breathing.

"Okay, Jamie, give it a try," he called to the small boy, who stood uncertainly behind the ladder leading up to the diving board. Then in a low voice to her, "A boy needs a male image to imitate."

"You chauvinist," she choked indignantly, and realized too late she had swallowed the bait whole.

"Watch me," came an excited voice from the height of the diving board, and the two of them turned their attention to Jamie, offering encouragement and then approval following his first attempt. He dived several more times before retiring to the shallow end of the pool while Kelly and his father engaged in an unspoken competition, diving time after time until finally she was out of breath and had to declare herself exhausted.

Blair pulled himself up beside her at the edge of the pool, so close his muscular thigh grazed her own. "You're pretty good." His voice held a subtle challenge. "Do you excel at everything you do?"

"I don't know about everything," she countered. "*Most* things, shall we say. You realize, of course, earning one's living cuts into developing one's leisure skills."

"Apparently it also sharpens one's tongue and develops one's class resentment," he quickly retaliated.

They eyed one another with both wariness and appreciation. It came as a shock to Kelly to realize how exhilarating she found this sparring session with him.

For a moment she had completely forgotten she was a lowly secretary and he her rich employer's son. She got quickly to her feet, intending to make a speedy exit.

That plan was immediately aborted, as Lady Jane was at that moment headed in the direction of the pool, followed by Sanford with a tray of drinks. "Sit down and have a drink, Kelly," she ordered. "You deserve it."

How drastically Kelly's aristocratic employer had changed since she had made it plain to her new secretary she could use the pool only when it was not in use by the family and guests. There was little choice now except to obey the command invitation, and Kelly draped a towel around her shoulders and settled into a comfortable lounge chair with her vodka collins. It was tall and cool and refreshing. She sipped it appreciatively, letting her thoughts drift while Lady Jane discussed several local happenings with her son.

When she brought her attention back to the present, Lady Jane was declaring, "Sorry, dear, but you'll have to find a replacement for me tonight, or go alone. I've had a very full day and there are still a few notes I want to get organized before tomorrow."

"The least you can do is order your secretary to take your place." Blair's words brought Kelly bolt upright in her chair.

"No," she said firmly, not even knowing what he was suggesting, but sure nonetheless that she had no intention of going anywhere with him. Not after what had happened just a few nights ago after the trip to the movies with Jamie. The enjoyable interlude in the pool hadn't changed the fact that he had humiliatingly rejected her that night.

"Why, that's an excellent idea. Kelly might enjoy going." From the reflective tone of her voice, Lady Jane might not have heard Kelly's refusal.

"Surely you're not declining an opportunity to dine among the cream of Palm Beach society at the famous and historic Everglades Club?" Blair's voice vibrated with challenge.

"Of course not," she intoned smoothly. "For someone like myself it's the chance of a lifetime."

His eyes locked with hers for a long jolting moment, and it was impossible to tell who won the battle.

Later in her room, Kelly was seized with trepidation at the prospect of the evening before her. Why had she agreed to spend time alone in Blair's company? Was she bent on self-destruction?

Catching a glimpse of herself in one of the full-length mirrors lining the tall doors of the *armoire,* she was amazed at the grimness of her expression. She might have been some tragic heroine attiring herself for a beheading ceremony in which she played the principal role! Her irrepressible sense of humor came to the fore, as it usually did, and she gave herself a rueful smile.

"Old girl, you won't win best dressed, but nobody will confuse you with the cleaning lady, either!"

The truth of that statement was indisputable, for Kelly looked lovely. Mentally she thanked her mother for a few basic values she had drilled into her daughters. One was an insistence upon simplicity of style. Another was the unshakable belief that no girl's wardrobe was complete without a "little black dress." In her early teens Kelly had accused her mother more than once of "living in the Middle Ages" and being "hopelessly old-fashioned," but inevitably she had to admit the wisdom of her unstylish mother's precepts of dress.

Tonight Kelly had fallen back upon her current "little black dress," which she automatically packed no matter where she went. It was a very plain dress, unremarkable in every way as far as drawing attention to itself, but extremely flattering on her with the exquisite blonde's coloring. Since she owned no spectacular jewelry and wouldn't dare wear anything fake to the Everglades Club, she took from her jewelry case a dainty little necklace her high-school steady had presented her at their graduation. Suspended on a fine gold chain was her initial K with a tiny chip of a diamond in the middle.

Fastening the pendant, she reflected that Dale Crater would probably make her a good, dependable husband if she decided one of these days to take him up on his marriage proposal. She had urged him more than once to marry a nice girl who would be content to settle down in Houma, a future she couldn't see for herself. According to her mother, Dale always asked about Kelly when he encountered either of her parents.

The light contact of the little necklace against her throat strangely bolstered her confidence. It evoked her past, that of an ordinary small-town girl doing the usual things, experiencing the typical growing pains and emotions, but wonderfully secure in the love of her parents and the knowledge of her own self-worth.

Aglow with an inner light resulting from that brief moment of sentimentality, Kelly was able to meet Blair downstairs with composure, never revealing her apprehension about the evening ahead. He was altogether devastating in a beautifully tailored white dinner jacket and dark trousers. His compelling blue eyes swept over her, not missing a single detail, including the tiny gold necklace, but he reserved any opinion he might have, complimentary or otherwise.

A half-hour later she realized the total absurdity of her earlier resolution to not be impressed by the Everglades Club. It had a grandeur that defied her powers of description. Part of its magnificence arose out of the pervasive aura of history, and she found herself intrigued with the background story Blair related.

"Paris Singer, one of the twenty-odd heirs to the Isaac Merrit Singer fortune, came to Palm Beach in the early 1900s and met up with Addison Mizner, who had some knowledge of architecture but reputedly couldn't draw detailed plans or write up a set of specifications.

What Mizner did have was a varied background, which had taken him all over the world, and a spectacular imagination."

Kelly stood beside Blair on a balcony overlooking a huge formal lobby. The wooden balusters of the railing were intricately carved and stained a dark brown. Huge beams running the length of the high ceiling were decorated in a rich design; gold contrasting with brilliant colors created a Byzantine opulence. Dazzling chandeliers shed light upon the dark polished wood and brocaded upholstery of the antique furniture. The rich green foliage in the great wooden planters gave a tropical ambience and softened the austerity of the immense room.

"It's hard to believe this place was originally intended to be a hospital," Blair continued, and then smiled at Kelly's incredulous murmur. "No joke. Singer commissioned Mizner to design a convalescent hospital for officers. He wanted to make a contribution to the war effort. By the time the place was finished—and it grew more and more grandiose during its construction—the war was over and Singer received less than fifty replies to the more than three hundred thousand invitations he sent out to veterans."

Kelly's face mirrored her sympathy for the disappointment Singer must have experienced after going to so much trouble and expense to perform a charitable service. Blair's blue eyes mocked her, and the undertone of challenge was back in his voice when he concluded, "Singer's wealthy friends convinced him *they* needed a place to go where they could relax in private, so in 1919 the convalescent hospital became the Everglades Club with Paris Singer the sole owner and soon-to-be social tyrant of Palm Beach society."

The tour of the club premises ended in a large dining room which had been reserved by a club member for the dinner-dance Kelly was attending in Lady Jane's place. The room was already filled with people. For an instant Kelly was seized with panic at the blaze of jewels and the profusion of designer gowns. What am I doing here? she wondered with a tinge of hysteria.

This must be the moment Blair Mathison had patiently awaited, when he could revel in her social inferiority. Surprisingly his expression showed no glint of triumph as he placed one hand firmly on the small of her back and guided her in the wake of the maître d'hotel who had greeted him with marked deference before showing the way to a table for four.

The two other people were already seated. Blair introduced them as Guy and Linda Hubble. Both appeared close to Blair's own age, early thirties, and it was soon evident that the three of them had known one another for many years. The Hubbles greeted Kelly with no more than normal curiosity, and she found herself reasonably at ease with them.

Blair explained that he had been giving Kelly a guided tour of the club premises, the reason for their being a few minutes late.

"The history of this place is really fascinating," Kelly offered in response to the expectant smile of Linda Hubble, a chic woman who would probably have been completely unexceptional in looks without her makeup and elegant designer outfit.

"Did he tell you my very favorite anecdote about the grand opening night?" Linda's voice bubbled with laughter and she looked delighted when Blair assured her he had not related that story.

"Mizner was unable at the time to import the antiques he considered appropriate. Instead, he improvised and made his own, resorting to the use of quicklime and shellac to make the leather upholstery appear antique. And, according to legend, they did look wonderful.

"On opening night, the ladies arrived in their finest gowns and most sumptuous jewels. Unfortunately, however, the heat from their bodies caused the quick-lime to soften the shellac and they became literally glued to their chairs! Mizner was occupied all evening pulling hysterical females loose from their chairs, and the next day the fragments of material indicated who had sat where!"

Kelly's spontaneous laughter rang with that of the other three people, whose familiarity with the story seemed to make it no less amusing for them. They laughed even harder when she glanced down somewhat dubiously at the seat of her own chair.

"Don't worry," Guy Hubble reassured, smothering a chuckle. "You won't stick to your chair tonight."

The hilarity broke down whatever social barriers Kelly might have anticipated, and she found herself surprisingly relaxed so that it wasn't necessary to pretend she was at ease in her surroundings. The elaborate meal was superb, beginning with shrimp remoulade and proceeding through cream of artichoke soup, lobster-stuffed tenderloin of beef, and ending with a dessert of fruit compote flavored with brandy.

A different wine accompanied each course, and Kelly's glass was replenished each time she emptied it. The alcohol contributed, no doubt, to her enjoyment of the meal and dinner conversation, which was never allowed to linger on topics from which she might be excluded. Whatever else she might criticize in Blair Mathison and his friends, they had excellent manners.

When the dessert dishes were cleared and coffee and liqueurs served to those desiring them, the music from the orchestra increased in loudness, signaling that it was time for the guests to enjoy dancing. Guy and Linda Hubble arose immediately, leaving Kelly alone with Blair at the table.

She could think of nothing sufficiently interesting to say, so said nothing, looking about her with genuine interest at the animated scene. Impeccably dressed men and chic women talked, laughed, danced and in general appeared to be having a good time. It was somewhat difficult for her to believe she was in this room with dozens of people whose names were famous around the world because of the immense fortunes amassed by their parents or grandparents in the days prior to antitrust laws and protective labor codes. Over in one corner she recognized a famous movie actress whose mother was one of the social lionesses of Palm Beach, heiress to a vast cosmetics empire.

"Pretty impressive, is it not?"

Kelly read the taunting challenge in Blair's question and turned her head to encounter directly the mockery in his eyes. Now that they were alone, he obviously was ready to resume hostilities. The deliberate arrogance in his whole attitude encouraged a counterattack, as if he wanted to goad her into some kind of derogatory statement about the scene before her.

"Yes, it *is* impressive," she answered with defiant honesty.

"Doesn't it make you wish you were born a Vanderbilt or a Firestone or a Post?" he gibed.

She ignored the sarcasm and considered the question seriously. "As intriguing as the thought is to an ordinary person like myself," she said slowly, not conscious that she lifted one hand and touched the tiny gold initial in the hollow of her throat, "I'd have to say no to your question."

His lips twisted in derision, but he said nothing.

"To wish I had been born someone else would mean that my parents, home, childhood, schooling, friends, *everything* would all be different. As impossible as it may be for someone like you to understand, Mr. Mathison, I wouldn't change anything about my background."

"Come now," he sneered, "don't be so polite, Miss Lindsay. Your middle-class self-righteousness is sticking out all over the place. You're secretly appalled at a life-style which not only allows but encourages self-indulgence."

She was deeply affronted by the insult in his tone, but an innate sense of honesty made her admit he was right. A life devoted to one's own pleasure and entertainment was quite beyond her comprehension. It seemed so wasteful and she told him as much.

"Now that we've established my middle-class narrow-mindedness, it leaves just one question," she announced coolly. "Why did you saddle yourself for the evening with someone of such limited capabilities?"

"I wanted to discover if you dance as well as you dive," he replied with breathtaking unexpectedness, and rose to his feet. "Shall we?"

She didn't know whether to laugh, taking his words as sophisticated nonsense, or refuse to get up from the table in the hope that he would feel like a fool standing there. In the end her own inbred good manners took precedence, and she allowed him to lead her to the dance floor.

One thing was immediately clear to her as the orchestra began a fast number with a Latin tempo. Blair Mathison was an excellent dancer, and she had to concentrate all her attention at first on following his intricate steps. Fortunately she had done more than her share of dancing in both high school and college, and she had no problem matching her movements with his. When the song ended, she was almost disappointed to have to stop dancing.

He made no move to leave the dance floor, though, as the music changed to a slow love song. Sweeping her close, he murmured, "Next you'll tell me you worked at an Arthur Murray studio."

Kelly was nonplussed at the cryptic comment, but inferred from it that he didn't find her lacking on the dance floor. Dancing close to him like this was something she definitely hadn't bargained for when she agreed to take her employer's place at dinner. The warm close strength of his arms around her, combined with the potently masculine scent of his aftershave lotion, had a devastating effect upon her. She felt as if she were no longer dancing but just floating in conjunction with his slowly tantalizing movements. Somewhat dazedly she decided to insist upon returning to the table as soon as this dance was over.

That good intention, like many more of its kind, was ill-fated and not to be carried out. They danced the next number and the next. After a while she stopped thinking and abandoned herself to the sheer sensual pleasure of his proximity on the dance floor. Her body obeyed his masterful direction as if the two of them had been practicing together for years.

Afterward, riding beside him the short distance back to Casa de Fresa, she felt like someone awakening from a drugged trance.

"Present from an old boyfriend?"

The abrupt question accompanied by a sharp sideways glance at first made no sense whatever. Then she realized she had unconsciously been caressing the small gold initial at the base of her throat.

"Uh-huh," she affirmed absently.

He didn't say any more until the car had rolled to a stop beside the towering mansion. Kelly felt like an awkward adolescent nearing the end of her first date, waiting apprehensively for the appropriate time to recite the traditional courtesy, "Thank you. I had a very nice time." Surprisingly she would have liked to say something of that nature to her now silent escort, but he would only make fun of her if she did.

"Are you engaged to the guy who gave you this?" With a quick movement he had turned sideways under the wheel and was leaning close to Kelly's face, touching the tiny gold K with an index finger.

"Not exactly," she said huskily, dismayed to feel a small nerve pulsing madly against the fingertip which had slipped beneath the minute pendant to caress the hollow of her throat.

"Holding out for someone who can afford a bigger diamond?"

It took a second or two for the insult, spoken in the same seductively low tone, to sink in. When it did, Kelly's anger erupted in a flash that temporarily blinded her. With a tremendous effort, she focused on the arrogantly handsome face with its leering smile and controlled the powerful urge to strike him. Somehow she denied herself the primitive thrill of swinging her palm hard against his flesh.

She met his eyes, just inches away from hers, and then flicked her gaze deliberately over his long form. "Why not? It even occurred to me when I took the job here that Lady Jane's bachelor son would make an excellent catch. Unfortunately your money isn't adequate incentive to marry someone as contemptible as you."

The forced cynicism in her voice seemed to echo in the tense silence as they glared at each other like two hostile animals.

"Maybe you need to know me better before you make any hasty decisions," he grated between clenched teeth. Before she could guess his intent, he seized her head with both hands, jerked it toward him and ground his mouth against her own. After a stunned moment in which she could do nothing to help herself, Kelly fought with the savagery of a wild creature, pushing with all her strength against his chest, and when that didn't succeed, she pounded her clenched fists against him.

Her struggles only seemed to further inflame his anger and intensify the brutality of his lovemaking. Gradually the harsh caresses of his mouth and hands awoke in her traitorous body a melting response, despite her fierce determination to continue to fight him. Against all the dictates of her outraged will, her mouth softened and moved under his and her hands slipped across his shoulders and up around his neck, exploring with rapture the firm muscles and thick, crisp hair.

What had begun on his part as an insult and punishment changed as she no longer fought him. The two former adversaries were pressing toward each other as if it were impossible to get as close as their need demanded, to touch and kiss urgently enough to satisfy the fiery passion consuming them.

Kelly was trembling and gasping for breath when Blair suddenly pulled away from her, thrusting her arms from around his neck and staring at her across the dimness. She observed that he wasn't any more composed than she, his chest heaving as if he had just crossed the finish line of a marathon course. He raked one hand through his hair and forced a harsh laugh.

"Well, maybe now you'll concede my point," he said huskily.

At the moment she wasn't at all sure what his "point" had been. Right now she just needed to get out of this car and away from this man whose touch affected her senses the way no one else's ever had. It was frightening to realize someone had that kind of power over her. Another few minutes of that abandoned lovemaking and she would have been begging him again to take her into his bed.

Her upbringing had never disparaged the importance of sex or presented it as anything shameful or dirty, but it had always been stressed as a meaningful act between husband and wife. Kelly wasn't able to cope with this unwanted new sexuality in herself. She didn't even like Blair Mathison. How could she, when he seemed bent on antagonizing her? Yet she couldn't resist the touch of his lips, the caresses of his hands, the thrilling closeness of his body against hers.

The only answer was for her to stay away from him during the weeks remaining before Lady Jane's party. As soon as that was over, Kelly would leave Casa de Fresa, return to New Orleans to her job at the television station and forget she had ever met Blair Mathison.

Chapter Seven

Awakening a half-hour later than usual, Kelly stretched luxuriously, recalling her first amazed inspection of this room she now thought of as her own domain. She had been positive she would be unable to sleep in the huge canopied bed, which looked like something more appropriate for a queen or a duchess at the very least, not for a girl from Houma, Louisiana.

How quickly she had adjusted to luxury, she reflected wryly, throwing aside the covers and striding barefoot over to one of the tall arched windows to gaze at the spectacular view, ending at the edge of the ocean. Bright morning sunshine added a cheery sparkle to the breathtaking vista.

More than anything else, she would miss getting up in the morning to this view. Her genuine regret shocked Kelly with its unexpectedness. Who would ever have thought such a twist of fate possible! When she left this estate and Palm Beach, as she would have to do very soon, she would miss her work with Lady Jane, her life at Casa de Fresa with all its novelty and unaccustomed luxury. And her friendship with Jamie . . .

What a joke on herself this whole venture had turned out to be. In an ironic way she was the victim of her own deceit. What was supposed to have been fake had turned out to be real, and what was real had lost the substance of reality. It was all too confusing. Only occasionally now did she remember the so-called "real" job she had come here to do, but it didn't seem nearly so important as it had at first. Heavens! Now that she thought about it, she hadn't contacted Stan Curtis even once to give him a report on her progress, nor had she seen Philip Lawson since that night at Gino's.

Recollection of that night brought the image she had been keeping firmly at bay on this fresh, beautiful morning. Blair! What an enigmatic, disturbing man he was. Just the thought of him made her breathless. Every second in his company had an electrified quality that made all her former relationships with men seem flat and stale. His attitude toward her was so elusive, changing from one moment to the next in a way that kept her constantly wary, unsure, and yet keenly anticipatory of his next move.

Last night . . .

She hugged herself tightly and gazed unseeing out the window. She had been so upset, at the end almost hysterical. She must have drunk too much wine, even though she didn't feel the effects of a hangover this morning. Alcohol had a way of making her emotional, which was one reason she so seldom ever overindulged. In the crystal light of day, she dismissed the panic of the night before.

"Face the facts, kid," she chided herself aloud. "Blair Mathison is a stunning male, and you're a perfectly normal female. Take those two ingredients, add wine and an evening of dancing, and what do you get? A romantic interlude which won't happen again. So don't worry about it."

Having disposed of her fears, Kelly hurriedly dressed for the day ahead, finally noticing that her dawdling and introspection were about to make her late. "And it takes ten minutes to get from my room to the main part of the house." She spoke the exaggeration aloud to the stone walls of the tower as she tripped down the stairs and then wondered at herself for this habit of talking aloud which she was developing. What was there to feel so buoyant about anyway?

Lady Jane had a thick sheaf of notes for her to type. "I should be back here some time after lunch. Maybe by then you will have finished these. In the meantime, the lights you need will be delivered." Her voice was matter-of-fact as she made this last prediction.

Kelly's skepticism showed in her face, but she reserved the opinion that even Lady Jane could hardly expect that kind of miraculous service. Nonetheless, by midmorning a delivery van had been admitted into the grounds, and an impressive array of professional photographer's lamps were carefully unloaded. Kelly was more than a little daunted at the realization she would be working with more lighting equipment than the typical small studio in Houma contained!

After lunch she loaded her camera with film, looking forward to a full afternoon of work. She would have to experiment with placing the lamps and the prospect appealed to her.

"What are you doing?" she demanded involuntarily at the unexpected sight of a tall masculine figure in the main hall examining the lamps, snapping switches on and off, twisting the adjustable shades this way and that.

Blair Mathison's raised eyebrows and sardonic grin brought a flush to her cheeks as she realized how sharply she had addressed the man who had more right than she to touch this equipment. She just hadn't been prepared for the sight of him in his Levi jeans and T-shirt.

"That is . . . I mean . . ." she mumbled, looking around somewhat desperately, as if hoping Lady Jane would appear.

"Miss Lindsay at a loss for words!" He dramatized mock surprise by placing his hands on his hips. She forced herself to meet the quizzical blue eyes but still found herself strangely unable to organize her thoughts adequately for speech.

Abruptly his manner changed as he informed her in a businesslike tone, "My mother called to say that she would be delayed. I've agreed to pinch-hit for her on one condition." He was undeterred by the doubtful expression on her face. "Shall we get started?"

"The condition," she reminded, dark eyes shimmering with skepticism.

"Oh, that!" He dismissed the thought with an airy wave of a tanned hand. "I have a decorating problem at the cottage you can help me with. It'll only take a few minutes, thirty minutes at most."

The picture of outrage at his clear insinuation, Kelly stood ramrod straight, her lips pressed together as she struggled for words scathing enough to express her contempt. Too late she realized she had once again fallen prey to a put-on. It was obvious in the glee of his laughter that he knew she had taken him seriously. Her own lips twitched into a grudging smile.

"Chalk one up for you," she said sheepishly.

"That's to pay you back for your snide comment last night about my money not being enough to offset my contemptible character," he said, sobering enough to speak. "Actually, I'm asking nothing more damaging to your character than a friendly game of tennis this afternoon."

Here was another subtle challenge, and in spite of her firm resolutions to keep her distance from him, Kelly found herself unable to resist it. What could happen to her right out on the open tennis court? "I think I should warn you," she said casually, tossing her head with a deliberate motion that shook her strands of silver-blond hair back from her face, "I'm pretty good."

He contained his astonishment admirably, her calculated audacity eliciting nothing more than a muffled gurgle to indicate she had indeed hit her mark.

"I've little doubt that you're good," he drawled in retaliation, allowing his eyes to speak their bold message as they roved over her figure. For a moment her self-confidence fled, panic overwhelming her at the insidious weakness invading her muscles and limbs as a result of his gaze. An impulse to turn around and flee came over her, but she found that she couldn't move.

The charged moment ended as precipitately as it had occurred. Blair swung around so that only his back was visible to her, the T-shirt taut across the width of his shoulders and the firm muscles of his back. When he spoke, it was to inquire impersonally about which rugs she planned to photograph first.

With an effort she answered and gradually was able to put aside the interlude from her mind. They worked very well together, and the afternoon passed quickly with no sign of Lady Jane. Kelly's absorption with the task at hand was so complete she was able to shut out the disturbing effects his nearness usually had upon her. Only occasionally as she stood to one side and waited for him to move or adjust the lamps would she allow herself to observe the way his jeans hugged his narrow hips and strained over his sinewy thighs as he moved about with lithe unselfconsciousness. If he was aware of her interested gaze, he showed no sign of it.

"Telephone call for you, Miss Lindsay."

Kelly maintained her crouched position behind the tripod and carefully clicked the shutter before straightening with a flex of her tired shoulders. "For me?" she inquired in surprise, conscious suddenly of an alertness in Blair.

She took the call in the library, thinking it must be Lady Jane calling to explain her extended absence this afternoon. But why had she asked to speak to Kelly? She knew Blair was here at the main house.

"Greetings, stranger." The masculine voice was immediately recognizable as Philip Lawson's. "How are things going?"

"You shouldn't have called me here!" Kelly controlled the strong impulse to whisper, which was, of course, ridiculous. She was alone in the privacy of the library. No one was listening at the door. That sort of gumshoe behavior existed only in movies and television dramas, not in real life.

"I was worried, since I haven't had any word from you in eons. Feared you might be locked away in a tower or some such equally horrid fate." Philip's urbane voice held concern, but underneath was the unmistakable hint of curiosity.

Kelly was at a loss for a response as she stood beside her desk in the library, receiver in hand. She didn't know what to say to Philip. In truth, she didn't even want to talk to him at this particular moment. His telephone call was an unwelcome intrusion, reminding her of obligations and ties to a world that seemed terribly remote just minutes ago.

"I've been very busy." How vague and distracted she sounded, even to her own ears.

"I can hardly *wait* to hear all the details." Something in his voice gave her an odd intuition that he already knew something about her activities at Casa de Fresa. And why not? He undoubtedly had many contacts in the area.

"Actually," he continued, "I have some rather urgent news from a good friend of yours in New Orleans. I had hoped you would be able to get away this evening and have dinner with me."

She knew he spoke with deliberate caution in the event someone in the house accidentally picked up the telephone and overheard them. But his cloak-and-dagger tone irritated her. The "friend" undoubtedly was her boss, Stan Curtis. A great tide of dread arose within her, mingling with exasperation, and she wished she could put Philip and Stan off a while longer, put the whole outside world off until she could sort out her thoughts and emotions. Why did Philip have to bother her now?

"Kelly—you still there?"

She sighed heavily, holding her palm over the receiver so he couldn't hear, and then succumbed to the quiet persistence in his voice. "Okay, Philip. I'm pretty sure I can manage to get away. Shall I meet you somewhere about eight?"

"Great. How about Gino's again?"

"No! Actually I don't feel like Italian food tonight," she added, regretting the involuntary sharpness of her refusal.

Philip designated another restaurant and then hung up, leaving her uncomfortably certain that he was anything but a fool and probably suspected her reluctance to meet him. There was no opportunity to mull over the telephone conversation or compose her muddled thoughts in preparation for the evening's encounter, for Lady Jane had arrived home in the meantime and sought Kelly in the library, inquiring as to what had been accomplished in her absence. Kelly could only surmise she had not talked to her son.

Just as Kelly was finishing her account of the afternoon's photographing session, Sanford tapped discreetly on the door Lady Jane had left ajar. "I beg your pardon for the interruption, but Mr. Mathison will meet you at the tennis courts in ten minutes, Miss Lindsay."

She felt suddenly as if the world were a gigantic merry-go-round which had accelerated with dizzying speed. She needed time to think, to collect her wits, but it wasn't allowed.

"Relax, Kelly," Lady Jane commanded, but underneath the imperious tone was a note of genuine warmth that only increased the upheaval of Kelly's emotions. "It will do you good to get some exercise. Now run along and don't keep Blair waiting."

Not a hint of disapproval that her secretary was meeting her son for a game of tennis, Kelly thought dazedly, hurrying to her room to change. Well, perhaps the best explanation was that Lady Jane had probably never denied her son anything, and whatever he sought in diversion was condoned by his mother.

There was little cause for deliberation over what to wear. Kelly had not come to Palm Beach with the expectation of playing tennis. She had packed several pairs of shorts, and now she pulled on one of them, tucking a sleeveless yellow blouse inside the snug waistband. Her canvas sneakers weren't proper tennis shoes, but they would have to do.

Blair was waiting for her at the tennis courts, which were encircled by a high wire fence that prevented the need for chasing balls. She entered the open gate and couldn't help but openly admire the tall lithe figure in dazzling white shorts and shirt. He looked up from a can of balls he was popping open, his eyes skimming lightly over her long shapely legs.

"What's the problem?" he asked warily, reading the sudden consternation on her features.

"I just remembered," she exclaimed, genuine dismay in her voice. "I don't have a racket." Her eyes followed his to a collection of at least a half-dozen rackets leaning against the fence. She could surmise from the cynical expression on his face that he thought she was trying to avoid playing against him. To cover her feeling of having appeared foolish, she walked over and knelt to examine the assortment of rackets.

He certainly hadn't overlooked any possibilities, she soon noted, selecting a wood racket with a perfect weight and grip. Had she wanted a metal or graphite frame, though, she would have had her choice! Her lips quirked at the corners as she rose from a crouched position, only then realizing he had been watching her the whole time.

Without speaking, she walked to one end of the court, a familiar and pleasurable tension rising inside her. With the casual solemnity of professional tennis players preparing for a match, they warmed up, practicing the full gamut of strokes from forehands and backhands to overhead smashes. Blair won the spin of the racket and elected to serve first. By then Kelly knew that he was a superb player and that she was fated to be soundly beaten, but she had no intention of giving up without a determined struggle.

She employed every strategy she had learned years earlier in junior tournaments and won a number of points from sheer refusal to concede, chasing down shots a less persistent player would hail as winners. In the early games, Blair allowed himself to be taken by surprise when balls he had judged beyond her ability to return came back to him.

They played two sets, with her taking two games in the first one and only one game in the second—no small accomplishment, considering his far superior power and expertise. At the end of the second set, they approached the net as if by mutual consent, leaning their rackets against it and toweling off. Kelly noted with satisfaction that his face was beaded with perspiration and his shirt clung damply to his lean torso. At least she had made him work for his victory.

"You're fantastic," she complimented generously.

"So are you." She couldn't detect a note of mockery to rob her of a flush of pleasure.

"How does a working girl from Houma, Louisiana, come to play tennis like you?"

Her startled eyes flew to meet his. How did he know she was from Houma? She didn't recall telling anyone, not even Lady Jane or the employment agency. Had the information slipped from her unawares?

"At age twelve, Billie Jean King was my idol. I took shameless advantage of some of my friends who belonged to a local country club and were lucky enough to take lessons from the pro. I insisted they repeat all his instructions and show me every single thing he taught them." She was rambling on in an effort to hide her confusion. "I don't play that much now that I—" She stopped abruptly, realizing she had been about to make a reference to her job at the television station in New Orleans.

His narrowed eyes were piercing in their scrutiny of her flushed features, taking in the soft fullness of the lower lip she nibbled between white teeth. To her immense relief, he ignored the incompleted sentence, managing once again to disconcert her with the totally unexpected comment.

"With a little practice, you'd defeat the best women club players in Palm Beach, including those at the Bath and Tennis Club who've had every advantage of professional instruction." He bent down to pick up a monogrammed leather racket cover and zipped it over the head of his racquet with brusque movements.

Now why had he said that? And why was he acting almost angry? She followed his lead and took her own racket over to the fence, where she placed it in the cover. Suddenly the probable explanation behind his cryptic statement sank in, rousing her ire. He was no doubt offended at the notion of a "commoner," a "mere secretary," mind you, being capable of competing with a member of his own privileged class. She remembered with disturbing clarity his grudging recognition of her ability to dive and then later to dance. It just hadn't occurred to her before that he could be that big a snob.

Completely incensed by her own interpretation of his manner, she stalked over to the gate and opened it with a vigorous clanging of the latch mechanism. "It was very *kind* of you to take time out of your *busy* schedule—" She tossed the words over her shoulder with withering sarcasm.

He reached her in two long strides, whirling her around and gripping her upper arms with a brutality that made her wince with pain. His blue eyes blazed down with a fury that scorched her helpless features.

"Sooner or later, I'm going to figure you out," he grated, administering a shake that made her teeth chatter and her neck snap painfully. She stared up with wide horrified eyes into a face so rigid in its blazing anger that she could discern the white bone structure under the taut brown skin. Her befuddled mind couldn't grasp what had unleashed the savagery of his reaction to her barbed words. She had intended to irritate, but not to this extent.

"May I go now?" she asked meekly, licking her dry lips nervously.

Immediately the cruel hands loosened and a swift change came over his rigid features. His eyes dropped to her moistened lips.

"What's the big hurry?" he asked huskily, his gaze moving lower to the noticeable rise and fall of her breasts under the clinging dampness of her blouse.

In this mood he was even more dangerous to her well-being than when he was angry, she realized with dismay, helpless to prevent the response of her body to the heat from his as he pulled her closer. The hard muscles in his thighs pressed against hers, and even though she arched her back to try to prevent the contact, her breasts pushed against his chest. His quick glance downward told her he too felt the hardening of her nipples under the thin layers of damp fabric.

"I have to go shower and get ready for dinner," she explained desperately. "I'm going out with a friend."

He displayed no surprise at this news, just a speculative expression in the blue eyes. "A male friend?" He lowered his head so that his lips grazed maddeningly along her cheek and lingered just at the corner of her mouth to tantalize and kindle little quivers of anticipation.

"M-m-m," she murmured, and moved her head sideways, her lips finding his to stop the teasing that was driving her crazy. He accepted the action as an open invitation, his mouth devouring hers with a hunger that quickly resurrected the flaming need she had come to expect when he took her into his arms. Her arms went up around his neck and she arched her body intimately against him.

After a while he was murmuring against her neck, his hot breath bellowing against her skin in little bursts of delicious sensation. "Why don't you just forget about this 'male friend' and stay here with me tonight?"

Kelly's eyes flew open, the soft haze in them gradually clearing as she completed his invitation in her own mind. If she stayed here tonight, there was little doubt that she would end up in his cottage! No, by far the safest move for her was to keep her date with Philip. What message did he have from Stan Curtis? The question brought back all the irresolution which had swamped her this afternoon when she had heard Philip's voice on the telephone. What was she going to do? How could she possibly satisfy all the demands, all the conflicting loyalties which tugged at her conscience?

Her sudden preoccupation must have been transmitted to the man who held her so closely in his arms because he raised his head and subjected her to a long probing stare. Then without a word of explanation, he released her and turned away to gather up the rackets, taking his time about it.

She was free to go, to escape the sensual enslavement this man invariably imposed on her. She was free to keep her date with Philip Lawson, her contact with the outside world, to which she would soon have to return. Why, then, didn't she *feel* free?

Lady Jane did not object to Kelly's going out for the evening, nor did she question her having made a friend since coming to Palm Beach. "Go and enjoy yourself, my dear. I do hope your present situation is as satisfactory to you as it is to me, but young people need the company of their own age group."

The words were transparent, invested with a meaning that did nothing to boost Kelly's flagging spirits. Lady Jane was really saying she wanted Kelly to be content in her job at Casa de Fresa. In her own way she was expressing her increasing reliance upon Kelly.

How much easier matters would be if her experiences at Casa de Fresa had worked out the way she had expected them to. If only Lady Jane were irascible and impossible to please. If only Kelly had been made to feel like an inferior outsider. Unfortunately none of this had happened. While she wasn't treated as a member of the family, she had all the comforts and privileges of a valued employee.

She mulled over these thoughts as she drove to meet Philip. He was curious to know about her observations behind the scenes in a Palm Beach household. Well, tonight she would tell him the truth.

"What a rosy, unrealistic picture you paint, Kelly! Come now, Stan Curtis is as much a realist as I am. He just won't buy that kind of fairy tale." Philip's voice was frankly jeering, his eyes narrowed as he regarded her through the cloud of cigarette smoke he had just expelled from his lungs. His attitude came as no surprise, but it was the match igniting her anger.

"It just happens to be true—every bit of it," she burst out. "I'm not saying Lady Jane isn't human. That she doesn't have faults. And I don't deny she's accustomed to getting her own way. But she's no sadistic monster, as you apparently demand to hear. Her employees are well-paid and treated with as much—no, *more* consideration than most workers out in the labor market. Every word of what I've told you is true!" Her dark eyes shot sparks of indignation. Philip's attitude was enough to make even her dislike journalists. No wonder so many people believed news people invented as well as reported the news.

"Hey! Hey! Calm down!" He held up both hands in mock self-defense. She noticed they were pale and delicate with sallow tobacco stains between the index and middle fingers. Blair's hands were brown and beautifully shaped with long supple fingers and very powerful, as she well knew. . . .

"I didn't mean to tick you off, but I'm not exactly a newcomer to Palm Beach, either." Philip's voice was conciliatory as he soothed her ruffled temper. Then subtly it changed. "This admirable loyalty toward the Casa de Fresa household doesn't have anything to do with Lady Jane's son, does it? Or the fact that he squired you to a fete at the Everglades Club last night?"

Kelly's eyes widened in astonishment. "How did you know that?"

He shrugged and postponed replying for the amount of time it took to raise the cigarette to his lips and take a deep drag. "It doesn't matter how. Suffice it to say I have my sources. What *does* matter is you, Kelly. I'm worried about you. If you remember, I tried to warn you at the outset of this venture not to fool yourself into believing you can ever be anything but a tool to people like Lady Wessen and Blair Mathison." His lips curled in derision as he said the last name, as if it left a bitter taste in his mouth. She wanted to probe the reason for such strong animosity, but he gave her no such opportunity.

"Stan made it clear in his call that he wants you to come on back to New Orleans, with or without the story. He's feeling responsible for you, having guilt

119

feelings for sending out someone as inexperienced as you to do a tough job."

She bristled automatically, then sighed wearily, one tiny portion of her mind conscious of how intensely he watched her. "I'm not going back until after the party," she stated flatly, and read the flash of speculation in his eyes. "My reasons have little or nothing to do with Stan or the feature," she went on candidly. "I owe it to Lady Jane to stay at least through *that* project." She was wondering bleakly to herself who would help her employer complete the work on the rug collection.

Philip surprisingly didn't take her to task for her admission. "This party you speak of. Is it the Hawaiian-style affair?" At her somewhat startled affirmative, he gestured impatiently. "No reason for alarm. You're not revealing any deep, dark secrets. It's an annual event." Then he questioned her in minute detail about the plans. Seeing no reason she shouldn't satisfy what appeared to be idle and harmless curiosity, she answered his questions, which were as specific as what catering service was being employed.

"You sound like a gossip columnist," she teased finally.

He wasn't listening, though. He was staring across the room as if glimpsing an apparition. She followed the direction of his gaze curiously and saw a small dark-haired woman standing just inside the entrance to the restaurant. Even from this distance she appeared overwrought, hands gripping her handbag nervously as her dark eyes roamed the room, not stopping the search until she sighted their table.

"Excuse me one moment, please."

Philip was out of the chair and across the room before Kelly could utter a sound. It might have been nosy of her, but she couldn't help watching the curious scene enacted before her gaze. Philip was obviously arguing with the woman, who kept glancing toward Kelly as if somehow she were involved in their dispute.

Kelly was reasonably certain she had never seen the woman before, but there was something vaguely familiar about her. The dark eyes a little too large for her thin, pinched features reminded her of someone she knew, but the association was too elusive to pin down.

Whatever the reason for the heated altercation, Philip was apparently the winner. The woman left as abruptly as she had appeared, and he returned to the table, his face an inscrutable mask.

"Jealous girlfriend?" Kelly made it convincing with the lightness of her tone and indifferent manner that she wasn't curious. Her own deep-seated horror of embarrassing scenes in public made her empathize with Philip in this instance.

"Something like that." He was entirely willing to drop the matter, but something underlying his smooth manner made her suspect he hadn't forgotten the episode. She sensed a tension like a tightly wound coil capable of springing loose at any moment.

His suggestion to go somewhere for a nightcap before she returned to Casa de Fresa was only half-hearted, and she declined with a genuine lack of interest. It might have been her imagination, but he seemed in a hurry as he escorted her outside the restaurant to her parked car. His quick glance around the parking lot contained an element of furtiveness that made her wonder if he feared the strange woman might be lurking about the premises.

On the whole, the evening had not been what Kelly had anticipated. As inexperienced as she was in journalistic work, she nonetheless possessed some perception about people, and Philip Lawson just didn't quite add up. His exhortations that she should not lose sight of her original purpose in coming to Palm Beach came across as perfunctory. And the keen interest in all the specific details of Lady Jane's party was puzzling, too.

What made her vaguely uneasy was the odd impression that Philip was more than casually interested in her presence at Casa de Fresa. Before her eyes flashed the picture of his face when he spoke Blair Mathison's name. The pale eyes had been malevolent. Then when he had argued with that unexplained woman, there had been controlled violence in his abrupt gestures, in the rigid lines of his body.

She shivered as the heavy gates of Casa de Fresa clicked shut behind her, a reaction prompted by relief rather than apprehension. She felt safer and dismissed her uneasiness about Philip as silly. If he called again, she would make whatever excuses necessary to avoid seeing him again. Something about him gave her the creeps.

The disturbing evening was temporarily forgotten when she guided the car to a stop in front of the garage and Sanford was nowhere to be seen. Now what was she going to do? She didn't possess a set of keys.

Deciding that he may have left a rear door unlocked for her entry, she followed the brick walk along the back of the house. She could hear the rhythmic surging of the ocean and smell the sharp salty tang in the brisk evening breeze. For a tempting moment she entertained the strong impulse to delay entering the house and go for a stroll along the lonely beach.

Common sense dictated that first she had to determine whether she was indeed locked out of the house. In that event, she had little choice other than to rouse either Sanford or Lady Jane. Of the two, Sanford was definitely her first choice.

The rear of the house was sufficiently lighted for her to find her way, but there was something eery about being all alone in the night, not a sight or sound to indicate the presence of another human being. The only sounds at all were the distant pounding of the surf and the shrill hum of insects in the shrubbery.

The door was locked, as she had more than halfway expected. "Darn!" she muttered disgustedly. There seemed little choice but to awaken Sanford, and she might as well do it as soon as possible. She had no intention of wandering around this monstrous house trying to locate a door accidentally left unlocked. For all her trouble, she would probably end up tripping off some sort of alarm system.

Just as she stepped down from the small portico to the brick walk and turned in the direction of the garage, out of the corner of her eye she discerned a movement in the darkness. Afterward she couldn't have said what made her panic the way she did. Perhaps the sudden overwhelming sense of terror was an aftereffect of the strange evening with Philip. The knowledge that she was locked out of the house and consequently quite vulnerable didn't help either.

She began to run, having some vague intention of jumping into her car and locking the doors. Then she could blow the horn, thereby frightening away the intruder, whoever it was, and hopefully attracting attention from those sleeping in the house and the garage apartment.

The movement *had* been made by a person, of that she was sure. Footsteps were pounding behind her in pursuit, increasing the urgency for speed. She might have had some hope of reaching the haven of her car if she had been wearing more sensible shoes. One high-heeled sandal caught on the raised edge of a brick and she lost her balance.

"You stupid little fool!" Hard hands gripped a flailing arm, jerking her upright and preventing her from falling. "What are you running from?"

"You!" she breathed, weak with relief to discover the unknown assailant was only Blair. She covered her wildly pounding heart with one shaking hand and took a deep breath.

"Were you trying to scare me to death?" she demanded unsteadily, beginning to feel a trifle foolish now at her headlong flight. "What are you doing here, anyway?"

Finally her mind began to function, assimilating the set of circumstances. "Did you arrange with Sanford to lock me out of the house?" Her suspicion hardened at the rakish grin on his face. "Well, your little scheme isn't going to work, Mr. Mathison. I intend to wake Sanford right this instant."

She turned to carry out her pronouncement. His hands grabbed her by the shoulders, jerking her back against him so that once again she was temporarily off balance. She struggled helplessly against the steel bands of his arms, which locked around her middle, holding her in very solid contact with his long, muscular frame.

"If you'll stop acting like a threatened virgin," he ground out, "I'll let you go."

The scorn in his voice released a fresh tide of indignation, but she stiffened her spine like a poker and stopped struggling. He immediately released her and took a step back.

"Are you denying you instructed Sanford not to unlock the door for me?" she demanded accusingly.

"So far I haven't had the opportunity to deny *or* explain anything," he countered with cutting sarcasm. When she maintained her resentful silence, he continued. "I informed Sanford that I would see you safely inside the house upon your return—and *not* for the purpose you're assuming." The latter assurance was prompted by her unladylike snort.

"I'm waiting to have my error corrected," she said with a prudishness calculated to irritate him. Her fright had abated and so, in actuality, had her hot burst of resentment. Now she was enjoying their verbal fencing.

He resisted the provocation. "I wanted to talk to you in private about something very important."

She couldn't detect the faintest hint of irony in his serious tone, but she had been taken in before. "Couldn't it wait until tomorrow?"

"It could. But I don't want my mother to know about it." His expression in the dim light was sober and he stood quietly awaiting her reply.

She shrugged compliantly. "All right. I'm listening."

"Good. Come along, then." He began walking in the direction of the terrace, and she followed, her reluctance mingling with her curiosity. But contrary to her expectations, he didn't climb the shallow steps to the broad tiled patio. She slowed her footsteps.

"Where are you going?" she asked suspiciously.

He glanced back over his shoulder. "To my cottage, where there are no sleeping people to disturb. Do you object?"

"You *know* without asking that I object," she blazed, as much in anger at herself as at him for the leaping of her pulse at the very prospect of being alone with him in the secluded cottage. "Surely we can manage a private chat in a house the size of this one."

They stared at each other across the few yards of darkness separating them. "Despite your irrational fears, I have no desire to drag you off to my lair, caveman-style," he said in a bored voice that made her feel foolish and defensive.

Deep down she shared his unstated opinion that there was nothing inviting about the cavernous chambers of the hulking mansion. Secretly she too preferred to go to the cottage, but she just didn't trust herself, nor him.

"Why don't we just walk?" she suggested tentatively, looking wistfully in the direction of the beach.

"Fine," he agreed shortly.

It wasn't really all that great an idea, considering Kelly's high-heeled sandals, which tended to sink into the thick lushness of the lawn. Finally Blair stopped, able to restrain his impatience no longer.

"Why the hell don't you just take those things off?"

"All right, I will," she agreed peevishly, and immediately did so. She wished she could take the panty hose off, too. Then she could walk with her bare feet through the damp stubbly grass.

"I promise not to look," he said with a note of exasperation.

Cheeks warm with embarrassment that he had read her mind, she reached up under the skirt of her dress and stripped off her panty hose. The night air curled deliciously around her bare flesh. She wadded the fragile nylon into a tight little ball and carried it along with the sling-back sandals in one hand as they continued strolling in the direction of the beach.

He didn't speak even when the smooth lawn ended and they walked down several steps formed by massive squared timbers to the sandy shore of the beach. Kelly was deeply conscious of the lulling beauty and sheer immensity of her surroundings. The pale uneven ribbon of sand stretched in either direction as far as she could see. The ocean, too, had no boundary out there in the shadowy distance, and up close it whispered seductively, sweeping in to curl around Kelly's bare feet and then drawing back provocatively, as if beckoning her to follow. Overhead the sky was fathomless, winking stars reminding her that there were other galaxies and the universe went on and on. . . .

"Did you enjoy your evening out?"

With difficulty she forced her thoughts to focus on his brusque question, resenting the introduction of such an unpleasant topic. "Not particularly," she replied honestly.

Like a speeded-up movie projector her mind went quickly through the sequence of events which had left her strangely uneasy. Now walking along the beach, she felt strangely detached and at the same time prompted by an inexplicable urge to confide in the man beside her. That, of course, was impossible under the circumstances.

"What did you want to discuss with me?"

He accepted the change of subject without comment. "It's about this damned party coming up. I don't mean to be an alarmist, but it makes me nervous just thinking of the possibilities of what can go wrong."

Kelly wrinkled her brow. "I'm afraid I don't understand what you mean."

He sighed. "The normal person doesn't. And before you go getting all huffy, that's *not* an insult." She was grateful for the screen of darkness. "No one will get through the gate," he emphasized the last word slightly, "without an official invitation, and there will be guards stationed down here along the beach."

"You're afraid of party crashers," she gasped in surprise, the thought never even having occurred to her before.

"I'm scared of party crashers, all right," he said grimly, "especially the kind with guns and stockings over their faces."

His meaning finally sank in, and Kelly's rounded eyes sought his face in the darkness as goose bumps rose along her bare arms at the alarming dangers his words had conjured.

"Not that I expect anything to happen," he reassured. "But there'll be enough jewelry alone at the party to tempt a saint, not to mention the numerous collector's items in the house itself. My mother insists upon having her treasures out where she can see them."

Kelly remembered her own uninformed speculation that the house must contain a fortune in Oriental rugs and tapestries. She supposed the same must be true for all the antique clocks, porcelain vases, figurines and other "knickknacks."

"I wouldn't know what to steal," she admitted candidly, and then wondered what there was in her remark to cause a long silence.

They were walking in the direction of his cottage. She hadn't had the nerve to insist on going the opposite direction, not after the initial fuss she had made. Now she saw they had arrived at the stretch of beach in front of his small front veranda. He turned toward the huge squared timbers forming the steps to the front lawn, and she followed behind reluctantly. He didn't mount the steps as she expected, but sat down on one of the lower ones, sprawled back on his elbows with his long legs stretched out in front.

Mindless of the danger of soiling her dress, she sat down too, leaving a safe distance between them. "What exactly can *I* do?" Even now that she perceived the danger, she didn't really see how she could prevent such things from happening.

"Keep your eyes and ears open during the party, for one thing. If you spot anything, anything at all that looks suspicious, let me know immediately. Don't be afraid of making a mistake and looking foolish. If your instincts tell you anyone—a waiter, musician, hula dancer, even a guest—isn't what he or she seems to be, I want to know about it. In the meantime, we're being very careful about screening those employed for the party. Another word of caution, the less that people on the outside know of the preparations, the better."

Kelly was very quiet, oblivious now to the spell of the tropical night as she recollected the conversation with Philip that very evening. She had told him everything about the party except the full guest list! Should she tell Blair now of her unintentional indiscretion. But she couldn't, not without opening the whole subject of her relationship with Philip.

"Oh, and another thing." The harsh note entering his deep voice rasped her already raw nerves. "Be on guard for the news hounds. Some of them have incredible gall and no respect at all for the privacy of others."

The rancor of that comment about members of her own profession killed any slight possibility of her confidence and brought back all the sweeping misery of her deception. If he had any inkling of the true identity of the girl sitting just a few feet away from him, he wouldn't be warning her in this conspiratorial manner. He would be throwing her bodily off the estate, she reflected unhappily. Why had she ever gotten herself into this terrible predicament?

She had come to Palm Beach with the blithe confidence that she could get a sensational behind-the-scenes view of the elite settlement and return to New Orleans unscathed by the experience. She hadn't counted on some highly unexpected complications such as developing a conflicting loyalty for her aristocratic employer, having her sympathies engaged by a lonely little boy, or falling in love . . .

What was she thinking? It couldn't be true! She just couldn't have fallen in love with Blair Mathison. But you have, refuted a forlorn little voice deep inside, and she could no longer deny the truth, as much as it shocked and appalled her.

She could understand the deep attraction she had felt from the beginning, even that first day when he had threatened to call the police and have her thrown off the estate. He was, after all, a handsome and vitally masculine man who constantly challenged and titillated her with his quick intelligence and ironic sense of humor. All that she could accept. But it was out of character for her to fall in love with a man who was an avowed playboy with no greater aim in life than to entertain himself.

In her present state of inner upheaval, the last thing she wished to cope with was Blair's physical closeness. But he moved across the distance separating them, remarking in a concerned voice, "Hey, I didn't mean to induce nightmares. I just wanted to warn you of the possibilities ahead of time—for your safety as well as everyone else's." One hand stroked the pale silky hair back from her troubled face, and she jerked her head away, alarmed at the tremulous weakness flooding her limbs at the gentle caress.

129

He ignored her recoil. "How about a nightcap before I walk you back? It'll help settle your nerves."

"No!" she objected swiftly, her heart taking off in response to the suggestive promise in the low voice.

"Exactly what are you afraid of, Kelly? Me? Or yourself?" He slid one hand along the graceful curve of her jaw and slowly forced her averted face toward him as if he hoped to read the answer to his soft question suspended in the emotionally charged darkness.

She squeezed her eyes shut, desperately marshaling her weakened defenses against the supple warmth of the hand still curved along her cheek, the thumb stroking the sensitive flesh of her neck. One part of her wanted to strain toward him, to encourage the descent of his lips against her own, which ached for his possession. But it was the deep-seated will to survive the perils of his lovemaking expertise that finally gained control.

"I'm not afraid of anything. I just don't want a drink," she whispered unsteadily, torn by the hope he would overrule her refusal.

"You're a fraud." The low words were spoken with a cold distinctness that slashed right through the shaky foundations of her composure. She teetered on the steep, lonely precipice of fear, trying desperately not to crash to her destruction.

Chapter Eight

"That's the last one!" Lady Jane's voice rang with satisfaction as she stated the obvious. Kelly had just snapped the final photograph of the sizable rug collection.

More than a week had gone by since the night she had returned to Casa de Fresa to find herself locked out, since the stroll along the ocean with Blair. During that time she had driven herself relentlessly, determined to keep too busy to remember that blood-chilling accusation, "You're a fraud!"

Still it rang in her ears night and day, haunting her with all its unexplained implications. At times she wished desperately she had reacted differently and demanded an explanation. Instead, she had blustered unconvincingly, "I don't have to stay here and be insulted by you," and retreated into a pretense of outraged silence to hide her shock and despair.

The walk back to the main house had been tense, her

nerves shrieking under the strain. They had not ex-,
changed so much as a parting word when he unlocked
the door with a savage grinding of the key and stood
stiffly aside for her to enter the quiet gloom of the
slumbering mansion.

She had been so dismally certain it was the end. That
somehow he *had* discovered her identity. The remainder of the night had been a waking nightmare as she
faced the exposure the morning was sure to bring. Had
there been any means of sneaking through those locked
gates, her cowardice might have gotten the best of her
as she anticipated the pain of facing Lady Jane.

Deep inside she was tormented by a sense of failure
she couldn't hope to explain to Stan Curtis or any of her
co-workers at the television station. In their eyes, she
would be deemed successful beyond belief in completing her assignment in Palm Beach. She had amassed a
wealth of information and taken more than a hundred
beautiful slides of Casa de Fresa, the grounds and its
inhabitants. She could put together a feature that
would bring her the recognition she had craved just a
few short weeks ago.

Her parents, though, would understand immediately
the shame she felt at having lived a falsehood. They
would be both shocked and disappointed in her, un-
swayed by glib arguments that nobody had really been
hurt by her thoughtless trickery. She would have to tell
them, too, as much as she might wish they would never
have to know how their daughter had ignored their
teachings of basic honesty and integrity.

Yes, she decided bleakly during those long hours of
soul-searching, she would tell them everything. Well,
almost everything. She would omit the terrible justice
fate had meted in making her lose her heart to Blair
Mathison. Someone had gotten hurt, all right, and that
someone was herself.

It was with relief that she dressed the next morning,
ready to face Lady Jane's anger and disappointment,

ready to get it all over. To Kelly's numbed astonishment, nothing whatever seemed to have changed in her relationship with her employer. That day work continued as usual. To make the agony of uncertainty even more excruciating during the days that followed, she had to endure the frequent presence of Blair, not only at meals but during the photographing sessions. He seemed to be well-informed as to her work schedule and managed to be on hand to assist in adjusting the lighting equipment. Without his help, she finally began to realize, it would have taken much longer to shoot all the pictures.

The probable truth behind his silence finally penetrated, dispelling her confusion. He didn't plan to expose her until he was good and ready and her immediate usefulness to Lady Jane was over. A slow anger smoldered inside her at the hypocrisy behind his cool manner. He had his nerve judging her when he himself was not above disregarding the personal feelings of another human being. It was vicious emotional blackmail, subjecting her to the uncertainty of never knowing when the sharp ax of exposure would fall.

The strain was becoming more than she could endure, compounded by the daily trial of being near him and concealing the devastating ache in her heart, which did not diminish in spite of his indifference or her own resentment. She hardly dared meet the inscrutable blue eyes for fear of broadcasting her own vulnerability.

Just last night she had decided to leave as soon as the report was completed. The party was only a week away, but she soothed her conscience with the reminder that Lady Jane had given countless parties without Kelly's help, and her money could ease any inconvenience caused by her secretary's abrupt departure.

And now that the last of the photographs had been taken, she would devote all her time to typing the explanatory notes. Barring unforeseen complications, she should be finished in two days' time. Her thoughts were so absorbed with these plans, she didn't at first comprehend her employer's words.

"Kelly! You're not hearing a word I'm saying."

"I'm sorry," she apologized, aware that her state of distraction had made her the focus of not just one, but two pairs of blue eyes. She fought the powerful temptation to look over in the direction of the tall masculine figure casually attired in old jeans and an open-throated chambray shirt. "What were you saying?"

"I want you to take the rest of the day off, child. You need to relax." Underneath the sharpness of the command was a note of concern that was Kelly's undoing. Tears smarted her eyes, making them so brilliant they seemed to illuminate the dark circles she had sought to hide with the painstaking application of makeup.

"But I want to type some notes this afternoon," she protested. "I'm not really tired at all."

"Nonsense. I won't permit it." Lady Jane's tone forbid any opposition. "You've been driving yourself, and it shows. There's plenty of time to finish the report after the party."

Kelly acknowledged temporary defeat but wasn't ready to give up the battle against time. "Why don't I take the rest of the film in to be developed?" In the back of her mind was the possibility that she might have to do some retakes.

Lady Jane mulled over this suggestion, a small frown lining her forehead. "All right. On one condition." She suddenly appeared extremely pleased with herself. "I want you to look for something suitable to wear to my party and charge it to me." She reeled off a list of shops on Worth Avenue that met with her approval.

"But that's not necessary," Kelly objected, alarmed at this unforeseen generosity. She couldn't blurt out the truth, that she wouldn't be needing a dress for the party since she wouldn't be present at it. "Nobody will notice what I'm wearing anyway."

Lady Jane didn't argue, and Kelly accepted her easy victory with relief. It wasn't like her employer to have her will overruled. A few minutes later, Kelly would be forced to admit the error of her assumption. When she emerged from the house expecting to embark upon her errand, she found Blair waiting for her behind the wheel of his low-slung dark-green sports car.

"Get in," he instructed.

"I prefer to drive myself," she objected stiffly, looking around in vain for the battered VW, which she had asked Sanford to bring from the capacious garage.

Inscrutable eyes flicked over her in the cool green sundress that revealed golden arms and shoulders. "You're wasting time. I'm acting under orders of my mother and your employer."

Sighing under the weight of the unavoidable, she moved with reluctance around to the passenger's side and climbed in beside him. "There's no need . . ." she began ungraciously, but the car was already moving. She turned her head away from him, staring at the beautifully groomed shrubbery and flower beds, the marble statuary and graceful fountains, all now a familiar sight. She tried to block out her awareness of him, tried not to visualize the confident brown hands on the wheel or the dominating profile with its strongly masculine jawline and firm mouth. In the brief instant she had permitted herself to glance at him, she had noticed how his crisp navy slacks were pulled taut over the muscles of his thighs, and she had had to restrain the crazy urge to touch him.

"Relax. I'm not going to ravage you," he said cuttingly.

Her head swiveled, dark eyes wide with indignation. "That was the *last* thought in my mind," she snapped, and saw the gleam of satisfaction in his blue eyes as they flicked over her outraged face, made a quick survey of her compressed lips and silvery blond hair falling softly from an off-center part to frame her high cheekbones and curving jawline.

"You sure fooled me," he needled. "I've had the impression you've thought of little else since that day I caught you eyeing up my bed."

For a second Kelly feared she would erupt with anger at his taunt. She understood for the first time the expression "saw red."

"I think you're the most conceited, contemptible man I've ever known," she breathed, hands clenched in her lap to keep from attacking him and causing an automobile wreck.

"That's too bad," he replied in a reasonable tone of voice, as if the girl beside him weren't trembling with frustrated anger. "Considering you're going to be seeing a lot of me at Casa de Fresa."

"No, I'm not," she blazed, and realized too late what she had said.

He made no reply, but the air between them crackled with tension. Out of the corner of her eye, she could see the dark frown contorting his brow, the firm mouth and jaw chiseled out of stone. Had he interpreted her words the way she meant them? That she wouldn't *be* at Casa de Fresa much longer? Suddenly she realized just how desperately she needed to get away from the exquisite torture of his proximity.

It didn't take long to drive the short distance between the estate and their destination, a photography studio in the small Palm Beach business district. Blair expertly maneuvered the car into a parking place in front of the establishment, undeterred by the fact that the two cars parked in front and back of the space had taken more than their rightful share.

Kelly was impressed with his driving skill, but would have died before she let him know it. He was too full of himself as it was. As soon as he turned off the ignition, she climbed out on the sidewalk, not waiting for him.

She might as well put aside her pique and get this errand over as quickly as possible.

He followed her inside the studio and stood distractingly close, hands thrust into his pockets and legs braced apart in a nonchalant masculine stance. The young woman taking down Kelly's succinct instructions concerning the processing of the film couldn't keep her eyes off Blair, and Kelly's voice reflected her sharp irritation at such feminine weakness.

"You were a little rough on her, don't you think?" The amusement in his tone brought her to an abrupt standstill out on the sun-warmed concrete of the sidewalk, and she forgot her recently formed determination to ignore him.

"You're . . ."

"Conceited and contemptible," he finished for her. "I think you've already mentioned those alleged faults in my character."

Despite her more-than-average height, Kelly would have had to tilt her head to meet his eyes, and she refused to put herself in the position of looking up at him. It was a strong temptation, though, because something subtle and unexpected had altered the awkward tension between them. The bantering tone in his voice warned her that he was enjoying himself, having for some unknown reason dropped the coldly indifferent air he had adopted with her since the night he accused her of being a fraud.

Despising herself for the fluttering weakness inside her midriff, signaling her appalling eagerness to respond to this first overture of friendliness in over a week, she said crisply, "Well, I hope the thrill of that poor girl's admiration has made this trip worthwhile for you. I'm ready to go back now."

"But you haven't carried out all my mother's instructions."

Puzzlement overriding pride, she searched his quizzical blue eyes. "I can't remember anything else," she said truthfully.

His gaze skimmed lazily over her, and her skin suddenly felt hot under the cool cotton blend of her sundress. An inexplicable breathlessness made her rounded breasts more noticeable for their rising and falling motion.

"Whew! It's hot! Why are we just standing here?" she blurted, and then blushed at the maddening quirk of his lips. How unendurable that he knew the way he affected her.

"We're waiting for you to be reminded that my mother has ordered you to buy something—'suitable' I believe was the exact word—for her party."

"Oh," murmured Kelly, dropping the screen of her long dark lashes. "I have plenty of time to shop for a dress later."

"The party's only a week away and you're going to find yourself busier than you believe possible."

She dared a quick look up into his face and read the determination in the implacable set of his mouth and chin. Her mind searched desperately for another excuse.

"You have no idea how long it takes me to shop for a dress." She laughed breezily. "Somehow I can't see you sweltering in a parked car for hours."

"I have no intention of sitting in the car," he corrected firmly.

She digested this information and then grasped at a last flimsy straw of hope. "Oh, you probably intend to come back later and pick me up. Don't bother. I can call Sanford or take a taxi."

He suddenly lost all patience with standing on the paved sidewalk. Even under the striped awning, it was quite warm, and the young woman inside the studio had been observing them with more than casual interest through the plate-glass front.

"I don't intend anything of the kind, or I wouldn't have bothered to drive you in the first place. Come on and quit procrastinating." He grasped her arm and began to pull her along with him as he strode purposefully in the direction of Worth Avenue, just a block away.

She half-walked, half-stumbled along beside him, trying to twist her arm out of the steel-fingered grip. If she hadn't been so exasperated at the turn of events, she would have perceived the humor of being jerked along like a recalcitrant child.

"Would you at least slow down?" she gasped. "And I'm perfectly capable of walking on my own!"

His pace slackened and the numbing grip on her arm eased, even though he still didn't altogether release her. They were passing in front of a small restaurant, and Kelly thought of a way to delay the shopping expedition a little longer.

"I'm dying of thirst. Could we stop here for something to drink?" She met his narrow-eyed suspicion with a dazzling smile.

"How could any man refuse?" he murmured, and held the door open for her to pass into the air-conditioned interior.

It was a bright elegant little place, the minute round tables a glossy white and the armless Vienna café chairs a pale shade of yellow. Numerous hanging baskets and wicker planters contained live plants rather than the dull plastic variety Kelly abhorred.

She requested lemonade and he ordered a glass for each of them. The service seemed unnecessarily swift, and in no time at all she sipped thoughtfully at the cool liquid.

"What excuses and evasions are you cooking up in that devious female brain of yours?" he inquired blandly, but his expression was watchful.

Resisting the strong temptation to take issue with the

139

implicit chauvinism in his statement, she demanded reproachfully, "Has it occurred to you that I have my own pride? Number one assumption is that I don't already have in my admittedly modest wardrobe a dress worthy of your mother's party. Number two is that I am willing to accept an expensive gift from an employer who pays me quite adequately for my services. And number three"—the petal-soft brown velvet of her eyes glowed with resentment—"that I'm incapable of selecting something appropriate without your supervision."

He appeared unmoved by the choked emotion in her voice when she enumerated the third and strongest objection. The suspicion had occurred to her that Lady Jane and her son didn't trust Kelly's taste enough to allow her to go shopping alone.

"Has it occurred to you," he countered acidly, "that you're being entirely willful and selfish in refusing to accept my mother's generosity in the spirit it is offered? She's expressing in the way she knows best a sincere appreciation of your work. The gracious thing for you to do is accept. The reason I came along was to make sure you didn't conveniently forget, as was nearly the case."

Kelly was trapped. His simple logic made her an ingrate if she continued to argue. The easiest course for her to follow would be to go ahead and buy a dress, which she could leave behind, still in the box, when she left. It could be returned and Lady Jane would be out no expense.

But the easy compromise sickened her. It was just another lie necessitated by the web of deception she had woven around herself. It was too late now to backtrack, to erase the painful reality of what she had done. But honesty had to begin somewhere.

She took a deep breath to give herself an extra supply of oxygen for courage. "The *real* reason I tried to avoid accepting Lady Jane's generous offer to buy me a dress is that . . . I won't be there for the party." She hadn't known that blue eyes could kindle into such icy flames and she flinched under their piercing scrutiny.

"And why won't you *be there?*"

His savage mimicry destroyed the thin veneer of composure protecting his raw emotions. Keeping her voice low so as not to create a spectacle for the benefit of the two waitresses and several other customers, she hissed at him, "I think you already know why I won't be there. *You're* the one who called me a fraud, remember?" He didn't take advantage of the small pause she deliberately left for his reply, but the intent blue eyes didn't leave her face for a second. "As you've already guessed, I'm not really trained to be a secretary and never should have presented myself as qualified. As soon as the report for the Smithsonian is completed, I plan to leave."

"Leave my mother in the lurch, you mean." He was following her example and keeping his voice carefully lowered, but his tone and expression broadcasted his scathing contempt.

"I *said* I'll finish the report—" she began, her anger rising to meet head-on with his.

"What about the party that's only days away? How about the inconvenience, not to mention disappointment, of coming to rely on someone and then having them take off without so much as giving notice? What's your dissatisfaction with the job anyway? Not enough money?"

She shook her head violently, suddenly struck mute by his reaction. She had braced herself for the anger and contempt, but certainly not for opposition to her leaving. He couldn't be suggesting she stay?

"Well, if it's not money, then what is it? Have you already grown bored with the enthusiasm you turned on when you encouraged my mother to do this rug thing? Are you tired of my son trailing you around like a devoted puppy?"

"Stop it! I won't listen to this!" Kelly pressed her

hands over her ears in a symbolic rejection of the horrible accusations. "None of that is true," she denied hoarsely.

"Then tell me your reason." His blue eyes probed relentlessly for the answer.

"You . . ." she began hesitantly, and stopped, not knowing how she intended to finish the sentence.

"Well, I can easily take care of that complaint." His voice was clipped, matching the icy chill that had replaced the heat of anger in his eyes and face. "It would be unforgivable of me to rid my mother of a prized secretary and my son of a favorite playmate just because you find my presence intolerable."

Kelly didn't dare try to correct his mistaken interpretation for fear she would clumsily reveal the truth. Wasn't his error actually the means of her salvation? If he avoided her, she would be able to stick it out at least through the party. After that, she would summon enough nerve to give Lady Jane notice of her intention to leave. By then she would have formulated a convincing reason.

"Finished your lemonade?" From his polite tone, the emotionally grueling exchange might seem never to have occurred.

Out on the sidewalk she turned automatically in the direction of the car. He grasped her arm. "Wrong way."

Then she realized that nothing said between them in the restaurant had changed his original purpose in accompanying her this afternoon. He meant for her to select a dress for the party and nothing could shake that determination.

What a maddening, inflexible man, she fumed inwardly, submitting to his iron will.

Worth Avenue was as picturesque and exclusive as she had remembered it from her first day at Palm Beach. Since that time, she had driven down the street numerous times past narrow shop fronts with bright awnings shading the sidewalks, but she had never browsed inside the stores, feeling more comfortable in the large shopping centers of West Palm Beach that catered more to the average shopper.

If she had expected Blair to stand by passively while she shopped for a dress, she was badly mistaken. He stopped in front of a dress shop Lady Jane had approved and held open the door, while Kelly sailed past him. The place even smelled expensive, and in the brief time she hesitated, he took charge.

The saleswoman approaching them changed from dragon to lamb at the mention of Lady Wessen and Casa de Fresa. Blair didn't bother to identify Kelly as his mother's secretary, and she sensed the curiosity under the woman's obsequious manner. It was Kelly's first experience with the VIP treatment in an expensive store.

The woman seemed more concerned with Blair's opinion than Kelly's as she determined the kind of dress Miss Lindsay "had in mind" and proceeded to show several models. Kelly instinctively showed a preference for the dresses that were sedate in style and color, having no desire to draw attention to herself at the party. It wasn't as if she were one of the invited guests. She would be there more in a working capacity. Blair's choices, however, were not guided by the same consideration.

When the time came for her to try on the dresses, she discovered to her chagrin that she was expected to present herself in each one for his inspection. If she hadn't felt so out of her normal element, she might have rebelled. Instead, she hid her discomfiture as well as she could and suffered the disturbing survey of blue eyes whose telltale gleam told her he knew very well how she felt. Had he promised only minutes ago to relieve her of his "intolerable presence"?

His preference was a tomato-red gown with a simple halter bodice that tied around the neck, leaving arms, shoulders and back bare. The fabric was a thin, silk knit that clung provocatively in all the right places, emphasizing the curve of her bosom and long slender legs.

She had been forced to discard her bra because of the style of the dress and Blair's lingering survey made no effort to hide his notice of that fact. Kelly was horribly afraid her cheeks must be nearly the same color as the dress.

He and the saleswoman were in complete agreement that the dress was "made for her," and with the barest pretext of consulting her wishes, the decision was finalized between them.

"But don't you think it's a little too—too . . ." Kelly protested feebly, confronted with her mirrored reflection in triplicate.

"It is definitely a little too," Blair agreed blandly, moving up close behind her and looking over her shoulder at the three Kellys. "That's the reason I like it."

His nearness and the intensity of his gaze was making the absence of a bra more noticeable every second. Kelly escaped to the fitting room, followed by the now benevolent saleswoman, who couldn't keep her admiration of Blair to herself.

"How is it that handsome men always have such good taste?" she observed with a rapturous sigh, and looked a little put out when Kelly didn't reciprocate.

Kelly had surreptitiously searched for a price tag in each of the dresses and found none. The desire to know was too strong to suppress. "How much does this gown cost?" she asked, and watched her social status drop fifty degrees in the woman's knowing eyes. The price was double her highest private estimate, and she reflected almost hysterically to herself that for the same sum of money she could replace most of her wardrobe of bargain purchases. Somehow the mental wisecracking helped her to assume a casualness she was far from feeling.

No money was exchanged. Blair signed the sales ticket and the dress was draped with great care amid swathes of tissue paper in a long box. He carried the box as they walked back to the car.

"I could get used to this," Kelly joked, trying to conceal her real feelings. She halfway expected a sarcastic gibe.

"Don't lose any sleep over the cost," he said quietly. "My mother can easily afford it."

She was too taken aback to answer. He had glimpsed beneath her pretense the real awkwardness she suffered. His remarks were calculated to put the gift in a realistic perspective, and she was genuinely touched at the gesture.

There was no conversation between them during the short ride back to Casa de Fresa, but the atmosphere was curiously relaxed after the earlier friction. Kelly thought wistfully of how wonderful it would be to know Blair Mathison under a different set of circumstances.

When they arrived at the house, Jamie was waiting for her. He came flying around the house attired in swimming trunks.

"Kelly, are you coming in swimming soon?" he implored, tugging eagerly at the handle of the passenger door.

"Sounds like a winner to me," she rejoined lightly, uncomfortably aware of the man beside her and his earlier suggestion that she had grown tired of Jamie's devotion.

The small boy hesitated for the briefest time. "You, too, Dad?"

Kelly appreciated the reticence Jamie had overcome in making the shy overture to his father, who unfolded his tall length from the car and stood looking at Kelly. In his eyes was a reminder of the assurance he had made her in the restaurant. He couldn't accept his son's invitation and keep his promise to stay away from her.

"Your father probably has more important

things . . ." she began, and then realized how unfair the words were to both Jamie and his father. "Maybe we can persuade him to join us," she amended, casting an apologetic look over at Blair. The last thing she desired was to widen the gap between him and Jamie, who needed his father's companionship.

"Miss Lindsay, here you are!" Sanford sounded slightly out of breath, as if he had been hurrying. "You're wanted on the telephone. It's long distance from New Orleans."

All the blood drained from her face, and she felt light-headed standing there, the focus of three pairs of eyes. No one seemed capable of speech for several electrified seconds. Kelly broke the spell.

"I'll meet you out by the pool, Jamie," she called over her shoulder as she hurried to take the call. Her voice sounded strange to her own ears, far away and dazed.

The caller was Stan Curtis, who didn't waste any time in conventional preliminaries. "Kelly, what's going on? Didn't you get my message from Philip Lawson?"

She heard a faint click somewhere in the vast network of connecting lines between herself and New Orleans, a world that seemed far removed from her at the moment. The nervous dryness in her throat impeded her normal speech.

"I explained to Philip that I felt obligated to follow through on a couple of projects here—" she began.

"What about your job?" he interrupted bluntly, his impatience a palpable force tightening her nerves into a hard ball in the pit of her stomach.

"Stan, it's all so different. I never should have— What I'm trying to say . . ." What an absolute idiot she sounded, certainly not an honor graduate in communications.

"Kelly, I want you back in New Orleans as soon as possible, and that's an order! I've been kicking myself for being such a fool ever since you took off on that damned assignment. Forget the whole thing and come home!" His deep authoritative voice cut incisively across the distance.

It occurred to her that he believed that the assignment had proved too difficult for her to manage, which wasn't really the case. For reasons unclear even to herself, she sought to correct his mistake.

"But, you see, I have the material for the feature, pictures and everything. It's just that I owe it to Lady Jane Wessen, my employer, to stay a little longer," she explained earnestly.

A busy man with many pressures and demands on his time, Stan Curtis had already exceeded the limits of his patience. The inconsistency of this last statement of Kelly's sent him over the brink into anger.

"Do I have to remind you that your *real* employer is Channel 10 in New Orleans? If you intend to keep your job, you'd better be in this studio by Monday afternoon at the latest. That gives you three days' traveling time, which is more than enough. I mean it, Kelly." She thought he would hang up, but there was a pause. "By the way," he said gruffly, "I can't wait to see if you're as lovely as I remember."

"Good-bye, Stan." She squeezed the words through a constricted throat that turned them into a strangled whisper and stood there after he had hung up, numbly clutching the dead receiver.

Now what was she going to do? If she remained at Casa de Fresa for the party, as she had allowed Blair to believe she would do, she couldn't be back in New Orleans until a week following this Monday, a week later than Stan's deadline. By then she would no longer have a job, real *or* fake. She was caught in a dilemma, and no matter what she did, she wouldn't be able to satisfy all her obligations.

What a mess! Tears of frustration burned her eyelids. How could she give up her job with the television station? It was a sensational opportunity, one her graduating classmates had envied. She had regarded it as a reward for all the years of diligent studying.

With feet dragging, she climbed the stairs of the tower, seeking the refuge of her room. She needed to think, but there was so little time. Her decision would have to be made without delay.

She wasn't even aware of how long she stood in the middle of the large room not really seeing anything. Suddenly she moved briskly toward the huge carved *armoire* and pulled open both doors. Her hand was grasping the handle of a suitcase stored away at the bottom when a small-knuckled hand tapped hesitantly on the heavy door of her bedroom.

"Kelly? Are you coming out to swim like you said?" called a hopeful voice.

Immobilized by indecision, she remained in the bent-over position, staring over her shoulder in the direction of the door, her lovely face contorted with pain. His last three words had stabbed her like a sharp knife.

"I'm changing into my swimsuit now, honey," she answered hoarsely, and dropped the plastic handle of the suitcase. "Fool!" she whispered savagely, and began to strip off her clothes.

Chapter Nine

Blair hadn't chosen to accept her oblique invitation to join herself and Jamie in the pool, and during the days following her decision to stay at Casa de Fresa, he kept his promise not to annoy her with his presence. She hadn't seen him at all since the afternoon shopping excursion. But in this case, out of sight definitely was *not* out of mind. His correct prediction that the days preceding the party would be hectic didn't keep her from thinking almost constantly about him.

Oddly enough, she gave little thought to her own personal predicament. Her mind went carefully over the account of his marriage and relived the passionate ending of that evening when he had told her of it. One part of her thanked God he had refused the abandoned offer of herself, while a shameless but honest part of her wished he had taken her.

As the day of the party drew closer, she remembered, too, the warnings he had uttered that night on the beach, and she was filled with unease. She tried to dismiss her feelings as the by-products of nervousness and an overactive imagination.

Scrupulously she heeded Blair's admonishment to avoid discussing the party arrangements unnecessarily with anyone on the outside. It was surprising how many people knew about the party and expressed idle curiosity when she charged large purchases to the Casa de Fresa account or arranged for deliveries.

A small incident reminded her of that one innocently indiscreet conversation with Philip Lawson. She was emerging from a florist's shop the morning before the party and saw Philip half a block away. Before she could muster an unenthusiastic greeting, he had checked his stride and turned abruptly to enter the nearest store.

He *had* seen her, of that she was sure. Why, then, had he avoided speaking with her? The answer she surmised made her contemptuous. Philip must have communicated with Stan Curtis and learned of her dismissal from the television station. That still was no reason to treat her like a social leper. Unless, she reflected cynically, he was afraid she would approach him for a job.

Well, he needn't worry about that possibility. She had no desire to be obligated to him in any way. A quick vision of him engaged in argument with the small brunette woman at the restaurant flashed vividly before her eyes, arousing the disturbing feeling she had had at the time that the woman reminded her of someone she knew. She shrugged dismissively. Today was no time to stand around chasing elusive resemblances, and if Philip wanted to snub her, she wouldn't lose any sleep over it.

"A picnic! You *must* be joking!" Kelly stared unbelievingly at her employer. "The party's tomorrow night!"

"I'm well aware of that fact." Lady Jane smiled indulgently at her secretary's distraught face. "But there's nothing more you or I can do until tomorrow. And I'm not thinking of you, to be honest. Eloise's regular day off is tomorrow, but because of the party she's taking today instead." She sighed, showing a trace of the intolerance with which she greeted any inconvenience. "Of all weeks for Jamie's school to dismiss classes for a teachers' conference."

Kelly's lips quirked at the implication of a pedagogical conspiracy. "It *was* thoughtless of them, wasn't it?" she inquired with mock solemnity, and was rewarded with a grudging smile. In the last week, Kelly had discovered in Lady Jane the hereditary source of Blair's sense of humor. When the older woman dropped the stiff, commanding manner, she was actually fun to be around, and the revelation had come as a surprise.

Without further argument about the outing with Jamie, Kelly went to her room and changed. The prospect of an afternoon sunbathing and romping with him on the beach definitely had its appeal. With a disdainful grimace, she pushed aside the brown one-piece swimsuit purchased for a role now completely abandoned and donned instead an apple-green bikini, covering it with an oversized T-shirt that made her feel and look like a teenager going to a high-school beach party. After thrusting her feet into her thick-soled rubber beachcomber's sandals and clamping a floppy hat on her head, she picked up her canvas tote bag, ready now to collect Jamie downstairs.

She could visualize him waiting with unconcealed eagerness. "Why does it take grown-ups so long to get ready to do things?" he always asked. The tender smile on her face at the thought of Jamie froze as she walked out onto the broad tiled terrace and saw the man sprawled in a wicker chair. Blair! And looking like a stranger in a severely tailored business suit! Her pulse drummed a wild reaction to the blue eyes which skimmed over her, making the voluminous T-shirt seem as provocative as if she wore nothing under it.

Questions crowded her head. Where had he been the last week? When had he returned? Why was he dressed like that, and why did he look at her this way, making her feel flustered and weak-limbed and so thrillingly alive?

"Where's Jamie?" She hadn't meant to sound so abrupt or breathless, and the struggle to regain her poise wasn't made any easier by his lazy drawl.

"Why, yes, it *is* nice to be back in Palm Beach. And yes, I did have a successful trip, albeit not a particularly enjoyable one. So nice of you to ask."

She flushed at the pointed mockery of her rudeness. Even in her confusion, though, his choice of words seemed oddly irrelevant. Sinking into the nearest chair, her legs rebelling against the task of supporting her body, she blurted, "Where were you?" Naturally she had assumed he was off somewhere skiing or sailing or doing whatever rich playboys like himself did with their time. What did he mean by saying he had a "successful" trip?

A cool arrogance settled over his features at her question, and she quickly retracted it. "Forget I asked," she said with a halfway convincing attempt at indifference. "Almost anywhere else was a wise choice over being here the last few days."

She couldn't fathom what in her words caused the sudden burning intensity of his gaze, which seemed to probe right into the secret depths of her soul. "So you stayed," he said softly.

Kelly had the odd feeling there was more than just surface meaning to his words, as if he knew what her presence here had cost her. But that was silly. How could he?

Now his manner underwent another quick transformation, and he smiled at her with a charm that stopped

152

her heart. Jamie arrived at that moment, accompanied by Lucille with the picnic hamper. Kelly didn't know whether to be relieved or frustrated at the interruption.

"I told Lucille to pack some extra sandwiches and some beer," Jamie announced importantly. "Dad's going on the picnic with us," he informed Kelly unnecessarily. His first statement had sent Kelly's eyes flying to meet the challenging confirmation in Blair's face.

"Only if your date doesn't object," Blair told his son.

Jamie giggled. "Kelly's too old to be my date, Dad. She's my friend, that's all." He was much too astute to have missed his father's intonation. "Is someone else coming with us, too?"

"I'm bringing a new friend of mine for you both to meet," his father admitted.

Kelly's blood boiled inside her veins. Of all the nerve! It was bad enough for him to barge in but to bring another woman along! She was much too angry to speak, and then she realized that was exactly what he expected her to do.

"Well?" His amused eyes noted her heightened color and set jaw.

"Well, what?" she demanded belligerently.

"Is it all right if I and my friend join your and Jamie's beach party?"

"It's your beach," she evaded ungraciously. "Come on, Jamie." She marched off, cheeks aflame at his low laughter. "Just don't forget the hamper," she ordered tersely over her shoulder.

Inwardly she fumed while making an effort to hide her irritation from the perceptive child, who glanced questioningly at her from time to time. Once they arrived on the beach, however, her surroundings forced her to relax, and she resolved that nothing would keep her from enjoying this afternoon, probably her last such outing with Jamie.

The whole scene was enchanting in the glittering sunlight. Overhead the sky was straight from a child's storybook, miles and miles of azure blue with little puffball clouds.

Before long, a perspiring Sanford plodded along the beach toward them carrying the picnic hamper with a blanket folded on top. Kelly's heart plunged to her toes at the realization that Blair obviously had decided not to come after all. Her disappointment made small talk difficult, but she managed to thank Sanford for his trouble. Jamie was too absorbed in the building of a sand fortress to take more than the most casual notice of either of them.

With brusque movements she spread the blanket on the sand, removed her hat, T-shirt and sandals and lay facedown. Dunce, she chastized mentally. He wouldn't have noticed you anyway, not with his "friend" along.

The hot sun blazing down on her slender form, covered only by the two strips of bright-green stretch fabric, gradually relaxed the tension bunching her muscles. She felt herself drifting off and murmured, "Jamie, don't go into the water without me."

He was oblivious to her warning, though, because he had just detected the figure of his father far down the beach and something small running along by his feet. The boy stared, holding his breath as he gazed down the beach. Could it be what he thought it was?

A few minutes later there was no doubt of it. With a shout of joy, Jamie abandoned the construction site of his sand fortress and raced along the beach toward the clumsy ball of fur scampering around the tall man's feet.

"It's a puppy! Dad, you brought me a puppy." Jamie knelt and gathered the squirming, pink-tongued creature against his bare chest.

Kelly leaped to her feet, jolted out of her slumber by Jamie's shouts, heart racing with fear for his safety. Then she saw him and understood. The puppy was the "friend" Blair wanted her and Jamie to meet!

The unrestrained joy shining in the little boy's face as

he brought the puppy for her inspection caused a large obstruction to fill her throat. Her eyes were drawn to Blair like steel to a magnet and found he was taking in her beach attire with undisguised interest. To cover her own acute awareness of his deeply bronzed body, clad only in the briefest of white swim trunks, she dropped to her knees to greet the puppy.

"Dad says he's all mine, and I have to take care of him," Jamie explained, the gravity of his responsibility only compounding his pleasure.

"He'll grow up to be a very good watchdog, too," she observed astutely, having noticed immediately that the puppy was a German shepherd.

"Smart girl." Blair's low voice came shockingly close to her ear. He had dropped down next to her on the blanket, so close that his bare warm thigh brushed disturbingly against her own.

Startled, she turned her head and found his face just inches away. Involuntarily she sucked in her breath, and his eyes dropped to the swell of her breasts only partially concealed by the top of her bikini. She was equally engrossed in admiring the smoothly muscled bare torso her hands ached to reach out and stroke.

"You look fantastic in that suit," he approved, completing his survey and bringing his eyes back to her face, where he divided his attention between her eyes and mouth.

"So do you," she blurted honestly, and then laughed along with him. He was the most blatantly virile man she had ever known, and the proximity of that powerful, masculine body did strange things to her.

Only dimly was she aware that Jamie had moved away from them a few yards down the beach and was playing with his new possession. At that moment she didn't care about anything in the world except the exhilaration inside her at the nearness of this man, whom she loved against all reason. They knelt on the blanket facing each other, his mouth tantalizing her with its firm promise, just inches away. The blue eyes were hazy with a desire matching the pulsing excitement rising inside her, but he made no move toward her.

Certain she would go mad if she didn't touch him, Kelly lifted both hands to his broad shoulders and traced their outline, feeling the gritty particles of sand between her flesh and his. His eyelids dropped so that his eyes were slits of molten blue passion, but still he didn't move. Slowly, as if pulled by a powerful magnet, she leaned forward and brought her lips against his, which felt very firm but unresponsive.

Too much under the spell of the strange fever spreading through her veins to stop now, she moved her soft lips against his mouth, tracing its bold contour. His warm breath fanned against her face. Without warning, something moist and hot flicked against her lips and with a helpless moan she parted them, totally unprepared for the sudden reversal of roles.

His mouth devoured hers, his tongue exploring and demanding, arousing hot flames of desire throughout her body but especially in those centers of pleasure of which he seemed unaware. Her arms had closed around his neck and her hands roamed his shoulders and back, delighting in the resilience of the brown skin covering the taut muscles. But his own arms remained lax, hands braced lightly on the blanket.

Kelly manifested her dissatisfaction with a protesting little sound deep in her throat. The pressure of his lips stopped, and with his mouth still against hers, he murmured, "Is something wrong?"

"Why don't you touch me?" she muttered, and felt his lips curve into a smile.

His response was immediate, as if he had been waiting for such a signal. The strong, knowing hands slid up over her thighs, shaped her hips and stopped for a moment at the trim bareness of her waist before coming up to tease the contours of her breasts, cupping the fullness just at the moment Kelly couldn't bear the suspense a second longer.

She wondered if he was feeling as much passion as she was. As if in answer to her question, he slipped his arms around her and hugged her hard against him, consumed with his need for her.

"Much as I hate to stop," he murmured huskily against her hair, "we have some rather wide-eyed company."

Kelly couldn't believe she had forgotten so completely about Jamie, who stood now a tactful distance away and approached the blanket when Kelly and his father pulled apart.

"I'm hungry," he announced, "and so is Rocky."

"Me, too," his father added, but his meaningful look at Kelly made clear the nature of his appetite. The answering surge inside her was so disconcertingly explicit as to her own needs that she immediately busied herself, delving into the lunch hamper to hide her confusion.

The afternoon was one she would long remember, perfect until right near the end. All her senses were keener than usual, making the food especially tasty, the canned soft drinks as intoxicating as champagne, the hues of sand, sea and sky brilliant beyond belief.

The three of them were in total harmony, whether talking, laughing, playing with the frolicsome puppy, or just lying quietly on the blanket attuned to the ceaseless rhythm of the ocean and the caressing rays of the sun. Happiness swelled Kelly's heart to the bursting point.

On the return walk to the house, she floated beside Blair, carrying her tote bag and the folded blanket while he managed the hamper. Jamie ran ahead, encouraging Rocky to try to keep up with him before finally scooping the puppy up in his arms.

A glance at Blair told Kelly his frame of mind during the last few minutes didn't match her own buoyance. "What are you thinking about?" she questioned gaily, and received a glance from his blue eyes where the recent warmth had disappeared behind a veil which hid his thoughts.

"Have you made up your mind yet when you're leaving?"

The words were an icy deluge dousing her unreasoning joy in the moment and bringing her back to cold reality. The way he had worded the query there was no question of whether she would leave, only *when*.

"As soon as the party is over," she said flatly, suddenly very battered and tired from the exposure to the sun and ceaseless ocean breeze.

"You haven't told my mother yet." It was a harshly worded statement, not a question.

"No." The simple truth was that she just hadn't mustered up the courage. She had even considered staying on as Lady Jane's secretary, but always that train of thought brought her to the necessity of explaining her original purpose in taking the job. After the truth was told, Lady Jane would never be able to trust her again. Always she would be wondering if Kelly was really just a journalist collecting data for future use.

Up ahead she saw Jamie arrive at the terrace, where his grandmother sat as if waiting for them to return from their beach outing. In another minute or two, it would be impossible to say anything privately to the tall bronzed man who had retreated behind his shell of cool reserve. The urgency of her emotions overcame her pride.

"Are you eating dinner with your mother tonight?" Realizing how close she had come to revealing the aching need to see him and be close to him in the short time left her, Kelly had asked the question in a stilted manner.

"Don't worry. I intend to keep my promise. You won't be bothered with my presence unless you'd like to visit me tonight at my cottage and take up our unfinished business."

The terse words were poison-tipped darts piercing the rawness of her exposed heart. What had seemed so beautiful and right between them on the beach was soiled by his insinuation. Her dark eyes glittered with tears.

"Too bad you didn't remember your promise earlier," she said bitterly.

"I did," he corrected. "Think back and you'll be forced to admit I didn't touch you until I was *encouraged* to do so."

"You're contemptible," she cried like a wounded creature, and dashed across the terrace past a startled Lady Jane and Jamie. The worst part of her humiliation was that his words were true. She *had* been the one to initiate the impassioned lovemaking on the beach. He didn't even have to touch her to reduce her body to quivering surrender.

She could only thank God that the party tomorrow night marked the end of his tyranny over her flesh, if not over her heart. She had to leave Casa de Fresa for her own salvation, although the strangling sobs which right now made breathing torturous indicated it might already be too late.

Chapter Ten

Eloise still had not returned by ten o'clock that night. Lady Jane's concern communicated itself to Kelly. Several telephone calls produced no clue to the whereabouts of the woman who had been Jamie's nursemaid since he was a newborn infant.

"Have you told Blair?" Kelly asked tentatively, wondering if Lady Jane suspected or had been told outright why her son hadn't joined them for dinner that evening.

"No. He probably won't be back from his engagement until very late, and I don't want to bother him unless I'm sure it's a matter for alarm."

Well, that certainly answered several questions for Kelly, but didn't make her any happier. The real reason behind Blair Mathison's absence from dinner had nothing to do with her, as she might have known if she possessed half a brain. No doubt he had a date this evening with some glamorous woman on his own social level, not a mere working girl of the middle class like herself.

"Don't frown so, dear. Jamie's old enough to spend one night alone."

Kelly didn't correct Lady Jane's error in reading her thoughts, but the notion of Jamie all alone in the suite of rooms he occupied with Eloise aroused her concern. He could have a nightmare and cry out and no one would hear him to offer comfort. He might be the heir to this enormous mansion and a huge fortune besides, but to her he was just a lovable small boy with all the needs and fears any child has.

Lady Jane offered no opposition to Kelly's wish to sleep in Jamie's suite. In fact, she seemed relieved. "That's very good of you, Kelly, and entirely typical, I might add."

What would happen to the warmth in her face and voice if she knew the truth? Kelly wondered bleakly. That the person she had hired to be her secretary was really a television journalist come to spy on her personal life. Make "television journalist" past tense, Kelly corrected herself bitterly, leaving Lady Jane's apartment and going to her own room, where she undressed and slipped into her pale-blue nightgown and matching peignoir.

The golden brownness of her skin, accentuated by the afternoon on the beach, was in startling contrast to her hair, like finely spun silver in the soft lamplight. She hadn't had her hair trimmed since she had come to Florida, and it hung longer on her shoulders now than its usual length.

Jamie looked even more vulnerable in sleep than awake, she discovered, taking care as she moved closer to his bed not to make any noise. A furry lump beside him drew her attention and an incredulous smile crossed her features. Why, the little scamp! Against all the clearly established rules to the contrary, he had sneaked downstairs and brought Rocky up to sleep not just in his room, but in his bed!

Reflecting that she would probably make a horribly indulgent parent when the time came, she nonetheless dismissed any thought of returning the puppy to his rightful place downstairs in a large storeroom. Eloise would be back tomorrow. Let *her* be the guy in the black hat, the expression Kelly's father always used to designate the villain in a movie.

Chuckling mentally at Jamie's daring, she looked around his room, lighted dimly by a lamp over in one corner. She had been in here before many times, once with her camera. But still she couldn't help thinking how unlike the normal child's room this was. The only appreciable difference between the furnishings here and those in the rest of the house was proportion, for there were no appliqués of dancing bears and cuddly baby animals in gay pastels. The carved and polished French antiques made Jamie's room the domain of a young prince destined to grow up and occupy his father's throne.

How many people knew that the heir apparent wasn't really his father's child? Certainly she would never reveal that knowledge, although Jamie was sure to know eventually. What difference did it make anyway? The parental relationship wasn't dependent on blood ties, or there wouldn't be such a demand for adopted babies.

What had Jamie been told about his mother? At his inquisitive age and especially with his intelligence, he must have asked questions. A sudden curiosity overwhelmed Kelly, and acting on impulse, she moved swiftly over to a child's desk. In one of the drawers, she found what she was searching for, a satin-bound album with BABY in embossed letters across the front. The handwriting on the first page confirmed her reporter's instincts: the neat squarish script wasn't Lady Jane's writing.

162

It had to be Eloise who took it upon herself to fulfill this duty rightfully belonging to a loving mother. All the information such as height and weight at the various stages of child development was duly recorded along with Baby's First Step and Baby's First Word. And there in the appropriate places were the pictures of his parents and grandparents.

Kelly took the album over to the lamp and stared down, stunned with disbelief, at the small photograph of the same woman she had seen arguing with Philip Lawson that night in the restaurant. Now she knew why the woman's face was so hauntingly familiar: Jamie looked like her!

Walking on legs that trembled with the shock of her discovery, she carried the album into Eloise's bedroom and sank into a chair, her mind a kaleidoscope of shifting images. The album seemed confirmation of Lady Jane's opinion of Eloise's dependable character and devotion to Jamie. Yet without any explanation, she hadn't returned tonight. Add to that the disturbing discovery that Philip was in some way involved with Jamie's mother—Blair's ex-wife—and had displayed an abnormal curiosity about the party tomorrow night. Then only this morning he had avoided speaking to her.

What did all this together mean?

It might mean nothing, but she had to tell someone, and the logical person at this time of night was Lady Jane. Then suddenly she remembered the care Blair had taken to warn her without his mother's knowledge of possible dangers the party might invite. He had been so insistent that she come to him and only him with any little suspicion, no matter how insignificant it seemed.

She jumped up quickly from the chair and rushed over to the telephone next to Eloise's bed. The receiver was in her hand and one finger poised to punch the raised buttons when she realized she didn't even know the number at the cottage! A quick look at her watch told her it was only eleven o'clock, which meant he might not be there anyway.

Dared she leave Jamie alone and go to Blair's cottage and wait there for him? Surely the sleeping child was safe for the moment. Case de Fresa was built like a fortress and all the doors were locked at night, as she well knew.

In her state of anxiety, she didn't give a thought to changing her clothes or replacing the satin slippers on her feet with more appropriate shoes. She did have enough presence of mind to grab the flashlight that the sensible Eloise kept within easy reach next to the telephone, no doubt in case of a power failure at night.

Tramping along in the dark through the grounds separating the main house from Blair's cottage didn't appeal to Kelly under ordinary circumstances, but especially not now. In her present state, the beautifully groomed shrubbery and rustling palm trees concealed all traces of unknown dangers. Once she tripped and fell headlong, having to retrieve the flashlight, which had fallen out of her hands. Not pausing to brush off the leaves and bits of debris clinging to her clothes and hair, she hurried on.

By the time she reached the cottage, she was gasping for breath, not just from exertion but from her raw nerves. Going automatically around to the front veranda facing the ocean, she noticed there was a light on in Blair's bedroom.

Her satin slippers made no noise on the wooden veranda, but the boards creaked under her weight. She pounded on the door so hard she bruised her knuckles and was rubbing them with the other hand when the door jerked open.

"What is going on?" His eyes narrowed, taking in her disheveled state and intimate attire in one raking glance.

She, on her part, was relieved to find him there after

all, yet the urgency of her mission didn't prevent her noticing that he wore nothing but unbelted jeans. The sight of his bare muscled torso brought back the disquieting sensations his physical nearness inevitably aroused.

"Lady Jane said you wouldn't be here—" Her breathless explanation was cut short as he reached out and gripped her shoulders, pulling her roughly against his masculine length.

"Save the talk," he ordered curtly, and before she could correct his obvious misinterpretation of her appearance at his door, he scooped her up roughly and carried her in the direction of his bedroom.

"But you don't understand," she gasped in alarm as he dropped her on the bed in which he had obviously just been lying. He paused a moment and frowned at her as she hastily smoothed the filmy chiffon over her exposed thighs.

"What is there to explain? I just can't quite believe my good luck." His words didn't explain why he seemed so angry.

"Please, Blair, let me explain," she begged.

His eyes were expressionless as they flicked over her disheveled hair, the golden smoothness of her skin exposed by her daintily feminine apparel, which more than hinted at the inviting curves underneath.

"I'm listening," he said tersely.

"Sit down. Please." She glanced uncertainly at the huge bed. "You're intimidating, towering over me like that."

He gave a harsh, forced laugh in response to her unspoken suggestion that he sit beside her on the bed. "If you really came to talk, I'd better keep my distance." He backed up and dropped into an Ames chair handsomely upholstered in cream-colored leather.

Kelly took a deep breath, blushed as his narrowed eyes took immediate notice of the rise and fall of her breasts, and then began her story with Eloise's failure to return that evening as expected. Within seconds she had his close attention, and except for an ejaculated curse at various points in her account, he did not interrupt. By the time she had finished, his face had paled to a sallow cast under the deep tan. When he didn't speak, lost in a frowning contemplation of her narrative, she began apologetically, "I guess it may actually be nothing—"

"No," he cut in brusquely, "you did the right thing coming to me immediately." This time the roughness of his tone wasn't meant to be offensive. "I gather I didn't mention to you before, when I told you the sordid little tale of my marriage. Denise's maiden name is Lawson."

"No!" she breathed in horror, her eyes rounded with this unexpected revelation and with questions she dared not ask, having risked far too much already. So far she hadn't explained and he hadn't asked how she came to know Philip Lawson.

"Lawson hates my guts in spite of the fact he's benefited in more ways than one from his sister's marriage to me."

"Not blackmail?" she whispered, realizing Philip must know that Jamie wasn't really Blair's son.

"Not for money. He knew better than to try that. But he managed to make some contacts through Denise that helped him get where he is today. I've left him alone with the understanding that he keep his mouth shut about Jamie."

"He wouldn't publicize something like that about his own sister, would he?" The prospect sickened Kelly, but not nearly so much as Blair's contemptuous reply.

"Lawson wouldn't be honorable in *any* line of work, but the one he happens to be in brings out the worst in most people."

What if he knew the girl facing him was in the same

166

"line of work" as Philip Lawson? The leaden weight inside her chest told her the dispiriting answer.

Suddenly he seemed aware of her despondency, if not its cause. "Don't look so worried. Thanks to you, nothing will come of whatever devious plot Lawson has cooked up. When I get finished with him, he'll be lucky not to find himself behind bars." There was a grim determination in Blair's voice and features.

He rose from the chair and came over to the bed, pulling her to a standing position in front of him. Then very gently he cradled her in his arms, stroking her fair hair and pulling bits of leaves and twigs out of it. She sighed and snuggled against him, rubbing her cheek against the rough hair of his bare chest and listening to his rapid heartbeat.

"Now that you're here, and so suitably dressed, I might just keep you," he threatened teasingly.

Alarmed at her quick response to the idea of staying here with him, sharing the intimacy of that mammoth bed, Kelly pushed away from him. "I'd better go back before Jamie wakes up and finds himself all alone—" A mischievous smile tugged at her lips as she remembered the puppy. Only after he promised not to punish Jamie would she reveal the cause of her amusement.

Suddenly Blair seemed in a hurry to escort her back to the house. She was grateful for his tall figure beside her on the path and perceived none of the lurking dangers so imminent a little earlier.

To her surprise he came with her all the way to Jamie's room. Then she realized he probably wanted to make sure for himself that his son was safe. It was very intimate standing next to him by Jamie's bed, watching the sleeping child with his furry new "friend" beside him.

Glancing sideways to see if he showed any signs of the same feelings, she discovered him watching her with a wry grin. Immediately she was intensely conscious of his virility, of herself dressed as she was and of the languorous weakness spreading through the network of her veins and arteries. It was as though the increased furor of her heartbeat slowed down rather than increased her circulation.

"Know what I'm thinking?" he whispered, laughter in his voice. At the slight negative shake of her head, he brought his lips down close to one ear as if to guard against waking Jamie. "I never thought I'd be jealous of my own son, but tonight I am."

His hot breath gusted against her neck and awoke a tremor of excitement. Then as if she willed it to happen, his mouth moved against her sensitized skin and his hands began to explore with tantalizing thoroughness the curves beneath the filmy chiffon. Her body must have been especially designed to be caressed by those expert hands, to fit perfectly into the unyielding contours of his masculine length.

Jamie, the puppy, Philip and his sister—everything faded away except his mouth hungrily seeking hers, his hands trembling with passion against her warm nakedness under the flimsy layers of material. With a low groan he pulled her against him as he had that afternoon on the beach.

Then he was shaking with laughter and she wanted to know what was so funny. He smiled down at her, white teeth gleaming against dark skin and his eyes kindled with mirth. "I was thinking of dear Eloise's face if she came home and found us making good use of her bed."

The image held more than just amusement for Kelly in her love-drugged condition, but her remiss conscience returned. Now was neither the appropriate time nor place for them to make love. Manifesting a self-control she conceded as far superior to her own, he kissed her quickly on the lips and was gone, moving with the lithe graceful stride that was one of the many things she found so irresistible about him.

What an incredible day it had been! Somehow everything had been done. All the colored lights had been hung, not just on the terrace but throughout the extensive rear lawns right down to the ocean. Twenty-five tables to seat four had been set up, draped in vivid red tablecloths, decorated with live flower arrangements and laid with heavy silver tableware and sparkling crystal glasses.

A large cabana-style structure had been erected just beyond the terrace, with a wooden dance floor and a conical thatched roof. The orchestra members were down there now tuning up their instruments, getting ready to play as the first guests began to arrive. The caterers were busy, too, unloading food from vans and setting it up on long tables whose decoration featured magnificent arrangements of fresh fruits and vegetables.

The waiters and waitresses were handsome young people in Hawaiian native dress and would dance for the guests' entertainment as well as provide table service.

Never in Kelly's wildest imaginings had she dreamed she would find herself present at such an extravagant affair. And even though she kept reminding herself she wasn't a bona fide guest, she couldn't restrain a rising sense of exhilaration. Part of that buoyancy was due to the anticipation of seeing Blair again. Even though she had not had a spare minute all day, she had still been disappointed by his absence from the main house.

After a final inspection of herself in the becoming red gown, which even she had to admit was "made for her," she went downstairs ready to do whatever she could to help things run smoothly. It had been very generous of Lady Jane to give her the bracelet; Kelly had found it in a long flat velvet box on her dressing table. To her eyes the brilliant stones looked like real diamonds, which, of course, they weren't. That good an imitation must have been expensive enough in itself, she thought ruefully.

The party was all she had expected it to be, the women resplendent in Paris gowns and jewels surpassing anything Kelly had ever seen even in a jewelry store. The men were urbane in sleekly tailored dinner clothes and more than willing to engage their hostess's lovely secretary in flirtatious conversation. Following dinner, she had no dearth of dance partners, either.

The one disappointment of the evening managed to dull all her pleasure. Blair might have been a polite stranger for all the notice he paid her. He seemed to be absent from the party much of the time, but when Kelly did catch sight of him, he seemed mesmerized by the lovely brunette girl who was his dinner partner.

At first Kelly was deeply puzzled and hurt by this unexpected behavior following last evening's intimacy. Then by intensifying degrees she became furious, concluding that it was all right for him to make love to her when nobody else was around, but he couldn't even be civil in the presence of his social equals. The knowledge stung bitterly.

Only once, late in the evening, did he approach her and ask her to dance. By then she was so incensed she turned him down frostily. He shrugged, his eyes dropping for an instant to the bracelet on her arm, and then walked off, leaving her to stand there and admire against her will the breadth of his shoulders under the white dinner jacket and his graceful masculine stride.

In spite of her relative lack of experience with such affairs, she judged the party to be an overwhelming success. Finally the last guest had departed, and the only ones left besides those involved in the cleanup were Lady Jane, Blair and herself.

"The best part of any party is talking about it when it's over," Lady Jane declared, her pleased expression making it plain she too deemed her party successful.

"Come along, both of you. Let's sit down and have a glass of sherry."

Kelly followed Lady Jane reluctantly into her personal sitting room, acutely aware of the tall silent man behind her. Lady Jane seemed oblivious to the tension between the other two as she settled herself with a sigh of relief into one of the stiffly formal chairs.

"Kelly, did I have a chance to tell you how beautiful you look tonight? I thoroughly approve of your choice of gown. How fortunate that you have a diamond bracelet which complements it so nicely."

At that moment Blair handed his mother a glass of sherry, and her attention was drawn away from Kelly so that she didn't see the incredulity illuminating the velvety darkness of her secretary's eyes. If Lady Jane hadn't given her the bracelet, who had? And wouldn't she, of all people, know the difference between real and imitation diamonds?

"The bracelet is a present from me, Mother," Blair announced quietly, succeeding in reducing Kelly to utter speechlessness. "Kelly is personally responsible for thwarting a plan to kidnap Jamie."

Now it was Lady Jane's turn to blanch, and it took Blair several minutes to explain to her satisfaction how Kelly's suspicions had alerted him to a plot between Philip Lawson and his sister to take advantage of the confusion during the party to kidnap Jamie.

Not until now did Kelly learn that Blair had enlisted the aid of the police in catching his ex-wife and her brother red-handed in the attempt. Both had left Palm Beach tonight with the threat of immediate arrest should they ever return. All that had gone on tonight, and Kelly hadn't suspected a thing!

Finally Blair had answered their questions, including those about Eloise, who had been lured by Denise to a house in a remote location, where she had been tied up and left helpless. The faithful nursemaid had allowed her sympathies to be raised by Jamie's mother, who claimed an interest in hearing about her son. Aside from being severely shaken, Eloise was just fine and upstairs with Jamie at that very moment, Blair assured them.

There was a long pause during which the three of them seemed very preoccupied with their own thoughts. Kelly looked up to find Blair regarding her with a strange intensity. His eyes remained fixed on her as he spoke.

"Mother, I think Kelly has something else to tell you."

Kelly stared at him, filled with a terrible foreboding at what was about to happen. All her fears of exposure seemed to come to a culmination in a moment she had been dreading for weeks.

"Well, Kelly?" he prodded, relentlessness in every line of his body. Unlike the two women, he had not taken a seat and stood now with his back to the fireplace.

"What on earth is going on here?" Lady Jane demanded, suddenly looking her age.

Kelly tried to speak, licked her dry lips and finally forced her speech through a constricted throat. "You seem to have the floor, Blair. *You* tell her." The husky words were underlined with resignation and bitterness.

Something like disappointment flashed across his blue eyes at her words. "If you prefer." He looked over at his mother, who was frowning in puzzlement at the exchange between her secretary and her son. "Mother, Kelly is leaving Casa de Fresa first thing tomorrow morning. She admitted to me a week ago that she is not a trained secretary and prefers to be released from this position. Under the circumstances, we both owe her a debt of gratitude and can only comply with her wishes."

His voice grated harshly on the last words, and for the first time, Kelly saw her employer at a loss for words. She looked from the forbidding expression on her son's face to the girl who had seemed to cower under the onslaught of his words but who stood now, making a visible effort to compose herself.

"What Blair says is true, Lady Jane. I'm not really a secretary, but I truly appreciate your kindness to me and I *have* enjoyed the work with you—" The stilted words cost her more in effort than anything she had ever done before in her life. With each passing second, a complete breakdown of her composure was imminent. "Would you excuse me, please!" she managed in a voice strangled with tears, and walked out of the room, head high.

In the room the first thing she did was unclasp the bracelet, a task made difficult by the uncontrollable trembling of her hands. Then she removed the exquisite dress, the most expensive garment she was ever likely to wear, and laid it carefully across the bed.

Next she changed into clothes that would be comfortable for traveling. Numbly, methodically, she lifted out her two suitcases and makeup case and packed all her belongings. When she had finished, she carried them downstairs and went to look for Sanford. He was in the kitchen with Lucille and didn't ask the first question or demur when she announced tersely that she was leaving immediately and would need her car.

Was she imagining things or was there a gleam of sympathy in Lucille's small eyes as she said, "Goodbye, now, Miss Lindsay," and in Sanford's polite voice as he bade her, "Drive carefully, miss."

The breakdown threatened again when she drove through the open gates and waited to hear them click shut behind her, terminating all relationships with the inhabitants of Casa de Fresa. For several moments she sat gripping the wheel, staring sightlessly through the windshield, before pushing the stick shift into gear and accelerating out onto Ocean Boulevard. She wouldn't give into her sorrow now. There would be time for that later . . .

The rest of her life.

Chapter Eleven

How long would it be before she could engage in normal everyday activities without this wrenching pain? Kelly wondered unhappily, unable to concentrate on the plot of the movie acted out on the screen. She had agreed to go out with Dale Crater more from consideration for her parents than anything else. They were concerned that after a month she still hadn't regained her old energetic spirit.

So far the evening had been an agonizing reminder of the past and a very different trip to the movies. Her memory operated entirely free of her will, which knew she had to forget Jamie and his father and stop torturing herself as she had tonight. She couldn't stop reliving each moment of that evening she had first seen the fun-loving humane side of Blair Mathison.

"Well, what did you think of it?" Dale's voice held none of the impatience he was fully entitled to display at her abstracted mood.

In appreciation for his tolerance, she made an effort to emerge from her mental lethargy. After the movie, Dale had suggested getting something to eat, and she had drawn a curious look when she said in a voice tinged with desperation, "How about pizza?" There was no way she could have endured facing a hamburger.

Now as they waited for their order to be prepared, she admitted to him that she had not paid much attention to the movie. "For one thing, my mind's too busy trying to decide what to do about getting a job."

"Why not take the job *I* offered you, at least for the time being?" Dale urged. His family owned the *Houma Daily News*, which had a large circulation not just in Houma but in several nearby small towns and the outlying rural areas.

Kelly was tempted, because right now it was the easiest course to follow, and she still needed time to heal. For the first time in her life she just didn't care about anything. Getting up in the morning held none of the joy and edge of anticipation it always had. But she couldn't just live off her parents, and besides, she knew enough about human psychology to recognize that she couldn't succumb to the lassitude threatening to overwhelm her.

"I'll give you a definite answer in the next day or two," she promised. If she took the job, he would have to understand it was a temporary agreement. She still had no intention of settling permanently in her home town, much as she enjoyed visiting under normal circumstances.

"If you take the job, even for a few months, you'll be doing the paper a favor by injecting a little fresh blood. And Kelly"—his kind brown eyes took in her somber expression—"you don't have to worry about there being any strings attached."

She smiled gratefully at him for putting into words

the reassurance she didn't really need now that she had seen for herself the full life, both professional and social, he had made for himself in Houma. He wasn't pining away for his high-school sweetheart, as Kelly's mother, with her romantic nature, had managed to construe from his inquiries into her daughter's whereabouts and endeavors.

The number of their food order was called, and Dale went up to the counter to pay for it and collect the tray of pizza and beer. Kelly's thoughts were free to wander to the telephone call she had received that morning. How on earth had a major television network learned of her opportunity to get an inside view of Palm Beach socialites? The only possibilities she could come up with were Stan Curtis and Philip Lawson, and neither of those was a satisfactory answer.

She had explained firmly that she had no interest in doing a feature which would be sold all across the country to local TV shows like *The People Element* in New Orleans. The man hadn't been ready to give up until she told him she had no photographs.

And she didn't. She had sent them all to Lady Jane along with a long letter which had tested all her training in the use of language. In it she had explained her deception and the change her attitude had undergone, bringing with it finally both guilt and regret. Striving for a positive note, she had thanked Lady Jane for her kindness and for enriching Kelly's life with a valuable insight into a way of life she had judged unfairly in her ignorance. Finally she expressed the somewhat wistful hope that Lady Jane wouldn't think too badly of her and assured her she had no intentions of ever making any journalistic use of her experiences at Casa de Fresa.

A week following her date with Dale, she left the *Houma Daily News* building, tired from a long day's work but feeling more like her old self. It was good to be so busy. There was no time for her to dwell on her own problems.

Parking her Volkswagen in the driveway of her parents' home a few minutes later, she noted with mild curiosity a rented car. Her parents hadn't mentioned expecting visitors.

Hearing voices coming from the den when she entered the house, she judged the visitors to be either close friends or relatives. Strangers were usually taken to the front living room, the one room in the house guaranteed to be presentable, since it was so seldom used. Her mother's forte definitely wasn't housekeeping.

"Kelly? That you, dear?" Her mother's query prevented Kelly from slipping unnoticed up to her room.

"The family reporter home from the office," she joked lightly, coming to a standstill in the open doorway to the den. The sight that confronted her was past all belief. Blair Mathison was sitting on the worn sofa, looking completely at home with her mother and father! Kelly stared, unable to move or speak.

"Sit down, dear," her mother ordered. "Blair was just telling us the Smithsonian was very complimentary about his mother's report on her rug collection."

"They were particularly pleased with the photographs," Blair added, watching her as she ignored the unoccupied space beside him on the sofa and went over to a worn wing chair. She had to remove Judy's blue windbreaker, Sunday's comics and a tennis racket before she could sit down.

There was a short awkward pause. Kelly finally found her voice, even though it sounded far from normal. "I'm glad about the report, for Lady Jane's sake. How are she and Jamie?"

Her eyes asked the questions she really wanted answered. Why had he come here? And what had he told her parents? She had already confided in them about everything that had happened in Palm Beach except the *real* reason she had come home so utterly devastated. That reason was the man sitting on the sofa as relaxed as if he dropped in on ordinary folks in Houma every day of his life.

After a few minutes of conversation, Bob Lindsay stood up and explained apologetically that he had to water his garden. His wife murmured something about a manuscript she needed to get ready for tomorrow morning's mail. At last Kelly was able to voice the questions plaguing her stunned brain.

"Why are you here? How did you know where I lived? Is there anything wrong with Lady Jane or Jamie that you couldn't tell me in front of my parents?" Her agitation increased under the survey of his familiar blue eyes, lit with a quizzical expression that made her pulse flutter wildly.

"Hey, one question at a time. But first, come sit down here." He patted the brown tweed cushion beside him, and she complied slowly, reluctantly, knowing what it would do to her to be so close to him but unable to resist the magnetic pull of his nearness.

He sat half-turned, his arm resting along the back of the sofa. She sat erect beside him, staring straight ahead until the urge to look at him became too powerful. Her wide brown eyes lifted to his masculine features, and she was filled with love for this man so far removed from her own world.

His eyes slowly traced her features and dropped to the open neck of her casual blouse. She had to say something to combat the sensations surging through her responsive flesh.

"Blair, why did you come here?" Her husky voice showed the strain she was under.

"Several reasons. Primarily to get some things set straight between us. To answer one of your questions, finding you wasn't difficult. If I hadn't known your

179

address already, I could have gotten it from your former boss at the television station in New Orleans."

Her face paled at his last words. "My parents didn't know," she stated despairingly, twisting her white-knuckled hands in her lap.

"I could gather that just from meeting them," he said tonelessly. "They're just not the kind of people who would teach their lovely daughter to be deceitful."

"It didn't seem like such a bad thing to do at first," Kelly said in a low voice full of misery. "The way Stan Curtis and Philip Lawson explained it, I felt at first like a visitor to an alien planet. I was able to rationalize my behavior by telling myself the idle rich like Lady Jane had been exploiting people all around them for generations and it was their turn to be used. . . ."

Her voice trailed off as she remembered how gradually she had found herself becoming fond of the autocratic woman and the small boy who so desperately needed the warmth of love and companionship. Her downfall had occurred when the people whom she had come to spy upon revealed themselves to her as human beings, in spite of the glamour and patina of their wealth.

"Why did you change your mind?" The question cut through her tortured memories.

She made an effort to get up from the sofa, instinctively needing to put distance between herself and the man eyeing her with his narrowed eyes. As if reading her mind, he captured one wrist with his long fingers.

"Why didn't you do the feature? God knows, you had enough information on all of us, plus pictures."

She took a deep breath. There was no way she could tell him the whole reason and save her own pride. "I just couldn't. That's why. Lady Jane was so considerate of me after we got to understand each other, and I just couldn't repay her by exposing her private life. It would have been disloyal. Please tell her that for me." She looked beseechingly at him and winced as his fingers tightened convulsively on her wrist, cutting off the circulation.

"You can tell her yourself. My mother wants you to come back to Casa de Fresa."

"Oh, no! I couldn't do that," she protested in horror, trying to jerk away from him but failing to pull her wrist free.

"Why not, if what you wrote in your letter to my mother was true? You said you enjoyed the association with her and your life at Casa de Fresa, so why not go back? Your parents assured me the job with the newspaper is strictly temporary."

She could feel his eyes on her downcast head and knew she would have to answer. How could she tell him that she couldn't bear to go back to Palm Beach, where she would be close to him and unable to avoid having an affair with him? Her kind of love required a more permanent kind of relationship, which was out of the question.

"Why can't you go back, Kelly?" Something in the low insistent voice, some seductively knowing quality, penetrated Kelly's troubled introspection. Why, he *knows!* she thought incredulously, and he wants to have the sadistic pleasure of hearing me admit the truth. She raised her head and stared into his impenetrable blue eyes, which probed hers relentlessly. What an incredible ego this man had, coming here to her own home and forcing her to admit she loved him.

"I'm in love with you!" she snapped, her brown eyes shooting sparks of anger.

His head tilted back and his laughter rolled out into the room. Then, without warning, he pulled her into his arms, crushing her so close against him that she could feel the hard warmth of his chest and the rapid staccato beat of his heart.

He chuckled softly against her silvery hair. "Life sure has been dull without you. I love you, too, you little impostor." The emotion vibrating in his deep voice released a tide of happiness that threatened to inundate her as she closed her arms around his waist in the effort to draw him even closer against her.

She murmured an inarticulate protest as he pulled slightly away from her, before she realized his purpose. His mouth came down upon hers with a searching passion that soon aroused a deep hungering need that would not be satisfied until he possessed her completely in that total union that would merge them into a physical and spiritual entity.

Their hands were insatiable with the need to touch and caress, the flame of their desire blazing to unbearable intensity. Suddenly Blair groaned and grasped her hands, which were inside his shirt. "If you don't stop that, in about ten seconds I'll be making love to you right on the family sofa." His voice was hoarse with restraint, and she realized just how aroused they both were.

"I'm sorry, darling," she murmured penitently, and tried to pull away.

"I'm not," he said, pulling her up on his lap. "My passionate young lady, I can't wait to get you into my lair. I want to gaze at you and kiss you." His voice was rough with suppressed passion, and abruptly he pushed her back on the sofa and stood up, his breathing irregular as he struggled to regain his control.

Now that Blair was no longer touching her, Kelly's brain had begun to function again. There still were some unanswered questions. "Blair, that night at the cottage, after we took Jamie to the movie, why—"

He sat down on the sofa again but did not take her into his arms. His eyes narrowed. "I wanted you that night, but . . ." He sighed deeply. "As painful as some of this might be to both of us, we might as well get everything out in the open. I didn't make love to you that night because you admitted you were innocent, even though seducing you was part of my plan for teaching you a severe lesson. I knew you were an impostor, a reporter meddling in other people's private lives, but I still couldn't bring myself to hurt you."

"You mean that even then you knew about me?"

He nodded grimly. "The first day, when I found you in my cottage, something told me you weren't what you claimed to be. But I would have checked on you anyway, without that intuition. Someone in our position has to be careful. Then, too, you showed such an interest in Jamie."

Kelly's soft velvet eyes glowed. "You thought I might be involved in some kind of kidnapping conspiracy."

His voice was apologetic. "That's always a fear, as I'm sure you understand now. At any rate, we keep an investigative firm on retainer, and with your car license number it didn't take very long to determine the real reason for your presence in my mother's household. I was furious at first and then puzzled. You just didn't seem the type, and I could have sworn you were genuinely interested in Jamie and my mother's projects. She was a new person after you turned her on to writing about her precious rugs."

"Why didn't you tell her the truth about me?"

He grinned ruefully and permitted himself to reach over for her hand. "I told myself I would handle it without upsetting her. Some pretty fancy self-deception, I'm afraid. I decided I would teach you a lesson you would never forget. Instead, the whole plan backfired on me. I'd never found a woman's company so stimulating, and before I could help myself, I fell head over heels in love with you."

Her mind went back to her last night at Casa de Fresa. "The night of the party, why did you ignore me? And then, later, in front of Lady Jane . . ." The recent memory constricted her face with pain.

The grip on her hand tightened as if he too were reliving that agonizing evening. "I knew the way I felt about you, and yet I still wasn't sure what you intended to do. During most of the party, my mind was preoccupied with what was going on in another part of the house—foiling the kidnapping attempt on Jamie. I think I didn't realize until then just how much he means to me, in spite of the circumstances of his conception. He's *my* son."

His words brought a deep joy to Kelly's heart on Jamie's behalf, but she didn't interrupt Blair to tell him that. She was too intent on what he would say next.

"I stayed away from you because it was getting harder and harder not to come right out and force the issue of who you really were. And I wanted you to tell me, *and* my mother, voluntarily."

Her tone was thoughtful with a new understanding. "That's what you hoped I'd do after the party, when you told Lady Jane I had something to tell her. And I didn't have the nerve. Oh, Blair . . ." She lifted eyes somber with regret and almost forgot what she still needed to clarify with him when she saw the unveiled adoration in his eyes.

Then she remembered another puzzle. "Why did you give me the bracelet? You know, I didn't even know those were real diamonds."

"For the same reason I bought you the dress for the party." His mouth twisted into the familiar wry smile at the protest on her lips. "Knowing your stubborn character, it was easier to let you believe I was simply carrying out my mother's orders."

"But why?" she breathed.

"Because I wanted you to feel comfortable at the party, and also because I have this incredibly strong urge to buy you beautiful things. Because *you* are so beautiful, and I adore you!"

She was deeply affected by the turbulent light in his eyes as they moved possessively over her. "But weren't you taking an awful chance? I could have taken your expensive dress and diamond bracelet back to New Orleans and written my assignment."

"That was the least of what I had at stake." He raked

his restless fingers through his hair, which had already been tousled by her eager hands. "Kelly, you've just *got* to understand. I had to make sure it was really *me* you want and not all the glamorous trappings. That's why I let you leave Palm Beach, why—"

He didn't have to finish his explanation. She knew now who was responsible for that telephone call from a major network offering her a tempting sum for a feature based on her Palm Beach experience. He had tested her ambition, which had taken her to Casa de Fresa in the first place, against her loyalty to Lady Jane and Jamie, and her love for him. The knowledge of his disastrous marriage helped her to understand his deep need to be sure of her sense of values. How glad she was that there honestly hadn't even been a struggle.

A deep note of joy rang in Blair's voice as he continued, "When I arrived in Palm Beach last night and my mother showed me your letter and all the slides you had taken at Casa de Fresa, you can't imagine the elation I felt. Since then, I kept reminding myself how you responded to me and prayed that you loved me the same way I love you—"

"Oh, Blair, I do love you so much," she murmured, aching to touch him, but mindful of the passion which had flared almost out of control a few minutes earlier.

He leaned forward and touched his lips lingeringly to hers. "I hope your parents won't be too disappointed, darling, if we forgo the big wedding and get married soon. Say, tomorrow?" The undercurrent of urgency in his voice echoed what she was feeling inside.

"My father used to tease me when I was about fourteen that when I got engaged, he would put a ladder outside my bedroom window and save himself the expense of a big wedding." The amusement in her unsteady voice brought an answering smile to his lips.

"A man after my own heart." He raised her hand to his lips and nuzzled the palm provocatively. "I just hope you know what you're getting into when you come back to Palm Beach. My mother is waiting impatiently to discuss the plans for the book she wants to write. Jamie probably won't let you out of his sight. And I expect you to accompany me on all my business trips. I haven't gotten any work done in weeks."

"Work," she exclaimed weakly, his lips brushing against her tingling palm, making it very difficult to concentrate.

"Work," he mocked, lifting her hand and rubbing it against his lean tanned cheek. "I suppose you still think I'm just a rich playboy living off the fruits of my forefathers' labors!" Seeing the guilty confirmation on her expressive features, he grinned wickedly. "I couldn't resist pretending to be what you expected me to be. You're marrying a very hardworking man, my darling. All those trips were business, not pleasure as you assumed."

She glared at him in mock censure. "You—you *impostor*," she accused before succumbing to the brilliant laughter in his eyes.

When their amusement had subsided, Blair framed her face with the strong hands she loved, hands that could be relentlessly cruel or incredibly gentle, as they were now. He looked into her eyes for a long searching moment and seemed deeply satisfied with what he saw in the velvet depths. His mouth smiled in the familiar wry manner, and she waited in keen anticipation.

"Hey—whoever you are—I love you."

Simultaneously they moved toward each other, finding it impossible to maintain the truce of physical separation.

Silhouette Romance

15-Day Free Trial Offer
6 Silhouette Romances

6 Silhouette Romances, free for 15 days! We'll send you 6 new Silhouette Romances to keep for 15 days, absolutely free! If you decide not to keep them, send them back to us. You pay nothing.

Free Home Delivery. But if you enjoy them as much as we think you will, keep them by paying the invoice enclosed with your free trial shipment. We'll pay all shipping and handling charges. You get the convenience of Home Delivery and we pay the postage and handling charge each month.

Don't miss a copy. The Silhouette Book Club is the way to make sure you'll be able to receive every new romance we publish before they're sold out. There is no minimum number of books to buy and you can cancel at any time.

This offer expires October 31, 1982

Silhouette Book Club, Dept. SBO 17B
120 Brighton Road, Clifton, NJ 07012

Please send me 6 Silhouette Romances to keep for 15 days, absolutely free. I understand I am not obligated to join the Silhouette Book Club unless I decide to keep them.

NAME_____

ADDRESS_____

CITY_____ STATE_____ ZIP_____

IT'S YOUR OWN SPECIAL TIME

*Contemporary romances for today's women.
Each month, six very special love stories will be yours
from SILHOUETTE. Look for them wherever books are sold
or order now from the coupon below.*

$1.50 each

Hampson	☐ 1	☐ 4	☐ 16	☐ 27
	☐ 28	☐ 40	☐ 52	☐ 64	☐ 94
Stanford	☐ 6	☐ 25	☐ 35	☐ 46
	☐ 58	☐ 88		
Hastings	☐ 13	☐ 26	☐ 44	☐ 67
Vitek	☐ 33	☐ 47	☐ 66	☐ 84

Browning	☐ 12	☐ 38	☐ 53	☐ 73
	☐ 93			
Michaels	☐ 15	☐ 32	☐ 61	☐ 87
John	☐ 17	☐ 34	☐ 57	☐ 85
Beckman	☐ 8	☐ 37	☐ 54	☐ 72
	☐ 96			

$1.50 each

☐ 5 Goforth	☐ 29 Wildman	☐ 56 Trent	☐ 79 Halldorson
☐ 7 Lewis	☐ 30 Dixon	☐ 59 Vernon	☐ 80 Stephens
☐ 9 Wilson	☐ 31 Halldorson	☐ 60 Hill	☐ 81 Roberts
☐ 10 Caine	☐ 36 McKay	☐ 62 Hallston	☐ 82 Dailey
☐ 11 Vernon	☐ 39 Sinclair	☐ 63 Brent	☐ 83 Halston
☐ 14 Oliver	☐ 41 Owen	☐ 69 St. George	☐ 86 Adams
☐ 19 Thornton	☐ 42 Powers	☐ 70 Afton Bonds	☐ 89 James
☐ 20 Fulford	☐ 43 Robb	☐ 71 Ripy	☐ 90 Major
☐ 21 Richards	☐ 45 Carroll	☐ 74 Trent	☐ 92 McKay
☐ 22 Stephens	☐ 48 Wildman	☐ 75 Carroll	☐ 95 Wisdom
☐ 23 Edwards	☐ 49 Wisdom	☐ 76 Hardy	☐ 97 Clay
☐ 24 Healy	☐ 50 Scott	☐ 77 Cork	☐ 98 St. George
	☐ 55 Ladame	☐ 78 Oliver	☐ 99 Camp

$1.75 each

☐ 100 Stanford	☐ 105 Eden	☐ 110 Trent	☐ 115 John
☐ 101 Hardy	☐ 106 Dailey	☐ 111 South	☐ 116 Lindley
☐ 102 Hastings	☐ 107 Bright	☐ 112 Stanford	☐ 117 Scott
☐ 103 Cork	☐ 108 Hampson	☐ 113 Browning	☐ 118 Dailey
☐ 104 Vitek	☐ 109 Vernon	☐ 114 Michaels	☐ 119 Hampson

Silhouette Desire
15-Day Trial Offer

A new romance series that explores contemporary relationships in exciting detail

Four Silhouette Desire romances, free for 15 days!
We'll send you four new Silhouette Desire romances to look over for 15 days, absolutely free! If you decide not to keep the books, return them and owe nothing.

Four books a month, free home delivery. If you like Silhouette Desire romances as much as we think you will, keep them and return your payment with the invoice. Then we will send you four new books every month to preview, just as soon as they are published. You pay only for the books you decide to keep, and you never pay postage and handling.

Silhouette Romance

Coming next month from
Silhouette Romances

Daring Encounter by Patti Beckman

Glamour, daring, mystique . . . Lord Richard Templeton had them all. And it was up to Andria to make America's top race idol an offer he couldn't refuse.

Devotion by Anne Hampson

Caryl's harmless masquerade backfired when Brad proposed to the wrong girl! Could she ever reveal herself and win his heart for her own?

Time Remembered by Lee Sawyer

His family had sent her father into bankruptcy years ago. But Sabrina couldn't deny the passion that engulfed her when Jules took her into his arms.

Game of Chance by Donna Vitek

Jason was everything Kit had ever hoped for, except that he was a gambler. Could she accept his profession, or would she lose the gamble—and his love?

An Ocean Of Love by Elizabeth Reynolds

He called her a gold digger and a fraud! Then suddenly, his attitude changed, and Jill found herself passionately in love with a man she didn't even like.

Yesterday's Bride by Susan Tracy

After years of separation, Leigh wanted to avoid seeing Jason again. But he lured her into his turbulent world, for she was his *wife!*

**Look for *Search For Love* by Nora Roberts
Available in July.**

READERS' COMMENTS ON SILHOUETTE ROMANCES:

"I would like to congratulate you on the most wonderful books I've had the pleasure of reading. They are a tremendous joy to those of us who have yet to meet the man of our dreams. From reading your books I quite truly believe that he will some-day appear before me like a prince!"

—L.L.*, Hollandale, MS

"Your books are great, wholesome fiction, always with an upbeat, happy ending. Thank you."

—M.D., Massena, NY

"My boyfriend always teases me about Silhouette Books. He asks me, how's my love life and natu-rally I say terrific, but I tell him that there is always room for a little more romance from Sil-houette."

—F.N., Ontario, Canada

"I would like to sincerely express my gratitude to you and your staff for bringing the pleasure of your publications to my attention. Your books are well written, mature and very contemporary."

—D.D., Staten Island, NY

*names available on request